HOVHANNES
TOUMANIAN

HOVHANNES TOUMANIAN

A SELECTION OF
STORIES, LYRICS, AND EPIC POEMS

Translated by
Dorian Rottenberg and Brian Bean

Edited by
Arra M. Garab

T & T PUBLISHING, INC.
NEW YORK

CONTENTS

HOVHANNES TOUMANIAN

(1869 - 1923)

Hovhannes Toumanian, one of the greatest Armenian poets, is a writer of universal appeal. His works with their classic simplicity and depth are intelligible to people of every age, nationality and time.

There are writers, and famous ones at that, who are not a man's lifelong companions, but only accompany him along a certain stretch of life's road, be it childhood, youth or maturity. But there are also writers that belong to all ages, from early childhood to venerable old age.

Hovhannes Toumanian is one of these.

The Armenian reader finds it as difficult to recollect his first meeting with Toumanian as his early infancy. He first heard him on his mother's knee, then as soon as he had learned his ABC, read them himself and gradually entered Toumanian's poetic world.

The poet wants the infant emerging into daylight to see life as bright and cloudless as joy itself. He approaches the child as a kindly spirit, to tell him about birds and foxes, dogs and cats, trees and flowers, to lead him along the wonderful paths of early knowledge.

"Spring came merry, the birds returned,
The sun rose warm, waters gurgled,
Days of plowing and sowing came.
I turned ravens into a team.
And harnessed geese as a spare one,
I hired sparrows to watch the herd,
And partridges to bake the bread,
I had a plot, I plowed and tilled,
I sowed barley and rye and wheat."
                                    (The Little Landtiller)

When they get a little older, junior members of society learn from the poet that the affairs of this world are not so cloudless after all, that there are good and evil forces in the world, and a constant struggle goes on between them, and that in their eternal strife good does not always triumph. The juvenile reader now takes up "A Drop of Honey," a legend (based on a medieval Armenian fable) telling how a destructive war breaks out all because of a drop of honey, and how at the end of it the survivors

"Asked each other terror-striken,
Where the world-wide great disaster
Took its origin, its sources."

The youth also reads "My Friend Neso," a story about how the best and handsomest boy in the village turns into a bad, dishonest man, dragged to the bottom by life's deprivations.

The youthful reader will probably derive the greatest benefit from Toumanian's masterpieces "In the Armenian Mountains," "Armenian Grief" and "With My Fatherland," poems which set the course for future Armenian patriotic poetry. Then come the stories "The Bet," "The Construction of the Railway" and "The

Deer." Next follow the great poetic canvases: "David of Sassoun," a brilliant rendition of the superb epic of the Armenian people; "Parvana," depicting the eternal yearnings of unquenchable love; "The Poet and the Muse," on the subject of the contradiction between the lofty ideals of poetry and harsh reality; "Sako from Lori," showing the destructive force of prejudice; "The Capture of Fort Temuk," which traces the criminal path leading from ambition to treason; and, finally, "Anush," rightly considered Toumanian's masterpiece.

In this poem the author expresses his philosophy of life, his personal ideas about man's existence, environment and the world of the human passions. The poet's nostalgia and his irrepressible love for his native land are revealed here:

> "My longing for that wondrous land
> Again and again it calls me back,
> And my soul on wings outspread
> Flies straight home where before the fire
> In my native hearth they are all awaiting
> Waiting anxiously for me...."

This poem, like every romance, has a tragic ending, and the poet, turning to Anush, roaming in solitude and despair at the loss of her lover, addresses her with words on the eternity of life and infinite renewal.

> "O fair lady, why do you cry
> So distraught and lonely?
> Why do you cry and wander
> In these valleys every day?
> If you desire fragrant roses,
> Wait for a while and May will come;

But if you long for your lover,
Know, he is gone, lost forever. . . .
Neither crying nor wailing
Will return your beloved;
Why then in vain extinguish
The youthful fire of your eyes?
Pour cold water from the fountain
On his lone and sorrowful tomb;
Go and begin another love,
That is the way of the world."

Toumanian's works are a living phenomenon in constant motion, a whole world swarming with countless heroes and buzzing with the sound of human voices. There is something we must know about Toumanian if we want to understand that world. Everything he wrote, prose and poetry, fairytales and realistic stories, even his journalistic writings and correspondence, has an inner unity, embraced as they are by the coherent world outlook of this great individual. Hence the extraordinary unity of his art, for all its great variety and wealth of tones and shades, a unity that is peculiar only to great artists.

Hovhannes Toumanian was born on the 19th of February, 1869, in the village of Dsegh, Lori District, to the family of Ter-Tadevos, an Armenian priest. Lori, or as ancient Armenians called it, the country of Gugars, was described by the poet Avetik Isahakian as a country of tales and legends, every corner of it a testament, each stone a witness to the heroic past. The poet spent his childhood in Lori, and that Homeric land left its indelible imprint on all his works.

Toumanian went to primary school in his native village. He was then a pupil at the Nersesian School in Tiflis, which he left early, leaving his future education and development to his own efforts, according to his tastes and preferences. That is why the famous Russian poet Valeri Bryussov could describe Toumanian as "largely self-educated, and an extremely well-read man if not systematically so," "a southern type in whom two principles, fun and genius, are astonishingly synthesized."

The rest of Toumanian's life, until his death in 1923, was passed in Tiflis, which up to the revolution was the administrative center of Transcaucasia, and a great center of Armenian culture.

He did not travel far, as did his elder friend Alexander Shirvanzade or his younger friend Avetik Isahakian. His trips were rare and made only when unavoidable. He once made a journey to St. Petersburg and Moscow, but that was a trip in a prison carriage in 1908, taking the poet to trial in court, accused of anti-tsarist activities. Towards the end of his life, in 1921, he travelled again; this time to Constantinople in connection with the work of the Armenian Relief Committee and returned with his health undermined. Lastly, towards the end of 1922, Toumanian, already seriously ill, was taken to Moscow for medical treatment, and it was his remains that were brought back to Tiflis.

If, despite the absence of salient events in Toumanian's own biography, he nevertheless lived a highly intense life, more so than any other Armenian poet, at least at that time, the reason must be sought in the environment in which he lived. Toumanian lived at a turbulent period in Armenian history. No other period in the long, tragic chronicle of the Armenian people is so dramatic, condenses so many splendid hopes and illusions and so much shattering disillusionment and tragedy as the end of the nineteenth and the first two decades of the twentieth centuries.

Toumanian was an eyewitness of and participant in all these cataclysms. He devoted his life to a country that had many enemies and few friends.

Toumanian engaged in numerous public activities. In the autumn of 1912 he sponsored the Caucasian Society of Armenian Writers in Tiflis and was chairman of this society up to 1921. The society organized weekly literary readings and public lectures devoted to Armenian, Georgian and other literatures.

In the three hundred old publicistic articles he wrote, Toumanian showed himself to be an accomplished critic and historian of literature and expressed many interesting ideas on literature, art, language and Armenian culture.

In 1917-1918 Toumanian sponsored a number of societies, Union of Countrymen's Associations, Society for Help to War Victims, Society for Help to Orphans and Refugees, and the Union of Eastern Peoples, which aimed at uniting the small nationalities of the Middle East.

Toumanian saw the supreme goal of art to be the bringing together of men, peoples and nations. He considered Shakespeare to have succeeded best in this and wrote of him: "He brings all people closer together, both to the English nation and to one another. And herein, indeed, lies the magic power of poetry and art in general: safeguarding the fragrance and charm of each in uniting them all, and from the many creating a harmonious whole."

We can proudly claim that Toumanian's entire work always has and always will serve that noble aim.

Dr. Levon Hakhverdian

POEMS AND LEGENDS

THE ANCIENT BLESSING

'Neath a hazel's green, gathered in a ring,
Sat the men of age, who had known life's sting.
They sat them around
Squatting on the ground,
For feasting and song,
This ven'rable throng,
Our fathers, the aged, our seniors, the sages
Honored for their age.
With uncovered heads we three of us stood;
We were school friends good,
Just three village lads, spirited and gay.
Our hands on our breasts in humbleness lay
As in voices strong we enlivened the throng
With song after song.
At the songs of joy of our childhood world
The grey Tamada his moustaches twirled,
Then each filled his cup to the very brim
And stood up with him.
This blessing they spoke: "Live long, lads, live gay,
Not as we lived in our day!"
The years have swept on — in earth they have lain,
The songs of our joy became songs of pain.
And I've called to mind as life I'd lament,
Their kindly intent.
This blessing they spoke: "Live long, lads, live gay,
Not as we lived in our day!"

Peace to your bones, our fathers who moaned!
The ills that you bore we also have known,
And now, in moments of joy or distress,
When children we bless,
We speak in your words: "Live long, lads, live gay,
Not as we lived in our day!"

1887

IN THE ARMENIAN MOUNTAINS

The way was heavy and the night was dark,
And yet we survived
Both sorrow and gloom.
Through the ages we go and gaze at the stark
Steep heights of our land —
The Armenian Highlands.

We carry from old our treasure,
Vast as the sea,
Brought into life
By the great soul of our people,
In our lofty land —
The Armenian Highlands.

How many times
The savage hordes
From the blazing desert
Tore and tormented
Our caravan
In our blood-smeared land —
The Armenian Highlands.

Yet, plundered and scattered,
Our caravan
Sought its way out
From among the rocks

Counting the scars of its countless wounds
In our mournful land —
The Armenian Highlands.

And we gaze with dolorous, longing eyes
At the earth in its gloom,
At the distant stars.
Ah, when will the dawn break at last
Over our green
Armenian Highland?

1902

THE CRANE

A crane has lost its way across the heavens.
From yonder stormy cloud I hear him cry,
A traveller o'er an unknown pathway driven,
In a cold world unheeded he doth fly.

Ah, whither leads this pathway long and dark,
My God, where ends it, thus with fears obsessed?
When shall night end this day's last glimmering spark?
Where shall my weary feet tonight find rest?

Farewell, beloved bird, where'er thou roam
Spring shall return and bring thee back once more,
With thy sweet mate and young ones, to thy home —
Thy last year's nest upon the sycamore.

But I am exiled from my ruined nest,
And roam with faltering steps from hill to hill,
Like to the birds of heaven in my unrest,
Envying the boulders motionless and still.

Each boulder unassailed stands in its place,
But I from mine must wander tempest-tossed —
And every bird its homeward way can trace,
But I must roam in darkness, lone and lost.

Ah, whither leads this pathway long and dark,
My God, where ends it, thus with fears obsessed?
When shall night end this day's last glimmering spark?
Where shall my weary feet tonight find rest?

1896

WITH MY FATHERLAND

From early days I turned my gaze towards the vast
    Unknown.
In heart and mind I soar above the abyss, intent
    and lone.
Yet every time, O country mine, my breast is torn
    again
When I reflect upon your past and present full of pain.
Upon the plight of ruined villages and burned
    and looted towns.

      O Fatherland beloved mine,
      In age-old sorrow you repine!

I see the ruthless enemy putting you to tortures,
I see your face so beautiful, your flowering
    fields and orchards
Contorted with the agony of villages and towns;
I hear the shouts of those whose name I calmly can't
    pronounce,
Who turned our land into a vale of sorrow without
    bounds.
Till now in plaintive songs, my land, that sorrow
    still resounds.

      O hillbound Fatherland of mine,
      In age-old anguish you repine!

Your wounds are countless, O my land, yet still
    alive are you.
The cherished words we have waited for are
    already breaking through

Your lips compressed with sorrow; we believe
    that on the way
Destined to you by God and Fate—those words
    you'll find and say.
We wait with fervor for your call—anon,
    anon we hear it;
You will become a promised land, free both
    in flesh and spirit,

      O lofty, sacred Fatherland,
      O ever-cherished Fatherland!

We hope, we know the dawn will rise and put an
    end to dark,
And joy will pour like sunshine into every
    stricken heart.
The summits of your mountains from the clouds
    on us will gaze,
And for the first time Ararat will smile
    at dawn's first rays,
And a poet with lips undefiled by rage and
    condemnation,
Will glorify in glowing words your great rejuvenation.

      O my reviving Fatherland,
      Shine with new light, my Fatherland!

1915

FAREWELL OF SIRIUS

O say, from what remoteness do you hail,
Sirius, mighty traveller of the sky,
What is the haven to which you sail
With speed untold
On endless routes,
As the centuries unfold?

Most brilliant gem of the firmament,
You gleam
On the heavenly dome.
With your bounty of ardent light
You decorate,
Illuminate
The canopy of our dim night.

How many eyes gazed at you before
Just as we do tonight,
And how many more
As yet unborn
Will be gazing at your light?

Who was it first wished you good speed
From our Earth
And the human race?
And in whose eyes without a trace
Will fade,
Darken, expire

Forever your farewell fire?
Good speed on your way, our ancient guest!
If you perchance
Meet mighty Death,
Ask her a question on our behalf:
"How many
Generations of men
Will a stellar leave-taking outlast?"

1922

REST IN PEACE

And I stood up, so that
In keeping with our ancestral laws,
I may read a last prayer
On the hapless victims of my nation,
Who in city and mart,
On hill and plain,
From sea to sea,
Extinguished are,
Dead, strewn, scattered
In their thousands.

And I borrowed fire
From the red flames
Of the great conflagration,
That consumed Armenia.
There in the bosom
Of the cold serene skies,
Ignited our mountains,
The Massis and the Ara,
The Sipan and the Sermantz,
The Nemruth and the Tandurck.

One by one I relit
The great candles
Of the Land of Armenia.
I relit the lamp

Of the Holy Arakadz too,
Like the distant sun,
Like the distant sun;
Endless and infinite.
Always refulgent and bright
Over my head.
I stood there sullen and alone,
Solid like Mount Massis;
I called upon those miserable spirits,
Strewn forever as far as Mesopotamia,
As far as Assyria, the Sea of Armenia,
As far as the Hellespont,
As far as the stormy shores of Pontus.

"Rest in peace, my orphans.
In vain are the bitter tears,
In vain and useless.
Man the man-eating beast
Shall remain thus
For a long, long time."

To my right the Euphrates,
To my left the Tigris,
With mighty torrential roars,
Singing psalmodies
Meandered through
Their deep, deep valleys.
The clouds, too,
Rose from the plain of Tsirac,
The giant censer.
They set out from the verdant hills.
From the Armenian Range.
Clumps fragrant,
Moved on and on,
Sprinkling the jewels of rain,

The scent of flowers,
The scent of incense.
As far as Mesopotamia.
As far as the Hellespont.
As far as the stormy shores of Pontus.

"Rest in peace, O my orphans.
In vain are the bitter tears,
In vain and useless.
Man the man-eating beast
Shall remain thus,
For a long time to come."

1915

ARMENIAN GRIEF

Armenian grief is a sea,
A fathomless, boundless main.
In that dark expanse drifts my soul,
Mournful, in mortal pain.

Now furiously it rears
And the azure coastline seeks,
Now weary it disappears,
Seeking peace in the deeps.

But neither can it find the bottom,
Nor can it reach the shore. . . .
In the sea of Armenian sorrows
My soul languishes evermore.

1903

BEFORE A PAINTING OF AIVAZOVSKI

1

The dishevelled waves
Of the sea,
Colliding
In foaming frenzy
Rear up
And gather themselves
With a fearful growl;
While in that vast
And boundless space
The raging hurricane
Howls.

2

Brush in hand,
The old magician,
Cries out, "Stop!"
To the wild elements;
Silent and docile
At the master's voice,
Those glowering seas,
At the height of their fury,
Freeze still upon the canvas,
Immobile in their motion:
Behold them before us!

1893

WITH THE STARS

O shining stars!
Eyes of the night,
Glowing ardent,
You smile so bright.
Just as you smiled
When still a child
Lively and brisk,
Bright as yourselves
I would frolic and frisk
Without sorrow. . . .
You smile today,
When weak and gray
I weep with grief
For my lost belief. . . .
You will smile tomorrow
Upon my grave. . . .

1891

WHEN SOME DAY

Sweet comrade, when you come some day
    To gaze upon my tomb,
And scattered all around it see
    Bright flowers in freshest bloom,
Think not that those are common flowers
    Which at your feet are born,
Or that the Spring has brought them there
    My new home to adorn.
They are my songs unsung, which used
    Within my heart to hide;
They are the words of love I left
    Unuttered when I died.
They are my ardent kisses, dear,
    Sent from that world unknown,
The path to which before you lies,
    Blocked by the tomb alone!

1894

ILLUSION

It started up, our true Chalak,
Raced across the mountain flank,
On and on through the darkened wood
With my bold brother in hot pursuit.

Glade and thicket they wandered through
In the twilight virgin depths.
I call them ever and anew,
Their return I still expect.

But alas, among our hills
Neither of them reappears.
Only their two voices still
Echo in my ears.

1918

DESCENT

For forty long years I follow one path,
Straight and fearless
Ascending
Towards a bright world, the Holy Unknown.

For forty long years by that dread path
I have travelled thus,
And now at last
Have reached
Tranquility.

I have left down there, at the mountain's foot
Glory and wealth.
Grudge and envy,
Everything that oppressed the soul.

And all the things
That I view again
From my mountain heights
Look so worthless and meager....

Now, richer in wisdom, my burden light,
With carefree laughter,
Song and canticle,
I descend from the mountain's other side.

1909

THE DOG AND THE CAT

1

Once there lived a pussy cat,
Who was very sleek and fat.
As for his trade,
Warm things he made:
Hats and mittens
For cats and kittens.
One fine day the furrier-cat
Whistling in his workshop sat
When in came a dog
Out of the fog.

2

He made a low bow
And he yelped "Hello!"
And after he'd yelped
He pulled out a pelt.
Then he said to the cat:
"Have a look at that.
I've got no hat
And the winter's near.
It's all too bad;
I'll freeze, I fear.
If it comes out nice,
I'll pay any price.
What do you say?"
"O.K."

3

"How long will it take?"
"Oh, less than a week.
To oblige a friend,
I'll be double-quick.
Sewing a hat
Isn't sewing a coat,
Oh no mere play.
Come on Saturday!"

4

"It won't be a hat
But a very peach,
The envy, I'll warrant,
Of every and each.
As for the money,
That can wait.
We'll talk it over —
Never too late.
Sewing a hat
Isn't sewing a coat."
"Good-bye, Cat!"
And off the dog strode.

5

On Saturday morning
The dog turned up,
Shaking and shivering
Like a wretched pup.
"Is it ready, my hat?"
"Oh no," he said.
"And where's the Cat?"
"Not at home yet."

6

Before the doorstep
On a mat
Frozen Mr. Doggy sat,
When down the street
Came Mr. Cat
In a brand-new lambskin hat.
He saw the dog and said:
"Waiting for me, I bet?
You'll be getting your hat, don't worry,
But don't be in such a hurry....
Though it isn't a coat but a hat,
It takes time, a job like that.
I sprinkled the pelt before tea.
Now I've got to cut it, you see?"

7

"Too bad," said the dog, "too bad,
That you haven't yet finished the hat.
But maybe you'll tell me plain
When can I see you again?
I'm coming here not to chat,
But to get my hat, Mr. Cat!"

8

"Come on Wednesday,
But please don't grumble."
The furrier-pussy mumbled.
So again the unlucky dog
Came on Wednesday at three o'clock.
"Good day! Now it's ready, I hope?"
"Good day! Lovely weather! Nope!"
But here their voices
Rose in pitch:

They told each other which is which,
And finished with a noisy tussle
Involving claw and tooth and muscle.
"You're just a thief!"
"And you're a crook!"
"She's just a bitch,
The wife you took!"
"You pig!"
"You brat!"
"You milksop, you..."
"You filthy cat!"
"I spit on you!"

9

Things went from bad to worse
Till it got to court, of course,
Where the Judge and Jury sat
Who promptly ordered:
"Summon
Both the dog and cat!"
The swindler cat
And swindled dog
Both came to court
At ten o'clock.

10

Who judged the case
And where and how
I see no need to say.
But ever since that famous row
The° furrier ran away.
He disappeared
And what is worse
Took with him
All his stock of furs.

And since the cheeky furrier
Of all our cats was sire,
To get their own back on the tribe
Is what all dogs desire.
On seeing one,
An honest pup
Starts growling at the cat
As if he wants to ask again,
"Well, what about my hat?"
The cat just hisses in reply
And spits from shame or fright
Just like the cat whose story I
Made up my mind to write.

1886

PARVANA

I

The high-throned Abul and Metin mountains
Back-to-back in proud silence stand,
Holding high on their mighty shoulders
Parvana — a beautiful ancient land.

And people say that there in his castle
Over the steps, next to the sky,
Lived a king, the hoary lord of the mountains
Who ruled Parvana in days gone by.

The king had a daughter, and such was her charm
That no one ever in his life did meet,
Hunting among the lofty mountains,
A doe so beautiful and so sweet.

His gray old age and his mountain realm
With her childish gaiety she adorned
And the old but happy King of Parvana
His darling daughter simply adored.

The years to come promised still more joy;
She came of age, and, legends report,
The king dispatched his ambassadors
To every castle and to every court.

"Where is," he inquired, "the courageous youth
That can win my daughter by main and might?
Let him don his armor and mount his steed
And come to take my daughter by right."

II

Their sabers clanged and clattered,
Their horses pranced and reared,
When before the castle
Those brave young knights appeared.

In front of the grand white castle
Of Parvana's hoary king
All waited in impatience
For the contest to begin.

Folk from all the neighborhood
Had left their hearth and home
To see who wins the maiden
For his very own.

The trumpet echoed. All the court
Assembled in the square.
Then came the gracious hoary king
And his daughter fair.

Her father came like a gloomy cloud
And like a moon came she.
Arm-in-arm, they were a sight
That all eyes were glad to see.

And all who gathered were amazed
That such a maid could be.
The brave young men stood silently
In spellbound reverie.

"Now look you at these splendid knights
All come to seek your hand.
Prepared to fight in contest fair,
Upon the square they stand.

"One will display his manly strength,
Another his skill with arms,
A further one his horsemanship,
Still another his grace and charm.

"And when the contest comes to end,
And they come to claim their prize,
And when the bravest of them file
In parade before your eyes,

"Then throw an apple to your choice,
The champion of the day,
And let the whole world envy you,
So happy and so gay."

The king was about to raise his hand
That the contest may begin,
When the princess set the apple by
And thus she spoke to him:

"What if a mighty-muscled knave
Beats a gentle-hearted dove?
He may be champion of the day
But never win my love."

Then asked the rivals gathered
Around the royal stand:
"What would a champion have to do
To win your heart and hand?"

"Is it wealth you want? We'll get you boats
With gold and silver laden.
Or is your wish a shining star?
We'll bring it down from heaven."

"No need have I for silver,
No need have I for gold.
And though you bring me gems and pearls,
You still may leave me cold.

"The man that is to be my lord
Must find undying fire.
Whoever brings the fire to me
Will have his heart's desire."

The gallant knights then took to horse
And gallop off did they.
Each chose himself a different road
And followed each his way.

They rode to fetch the princess fire
That would forever burn.
But though many years rolled by,
No one man did return.

III

"Oh, Father dear, where are the knights,
Why do they not return?
Perhaps it can't be found at all,
Fire that will always burn?"

"Yes, daughter dear, they sure will come
And bring undying fire.
But the roads and ways of dauntless men
Are full of dangers dire.

"They have to pass through evil ground
And in evil water swim,
And clash in deadly battle
With the spiteful Jinn."

Year after year went by again
But no one brought the flame.
"Look from the window, Father dear;
It's surely time they came.

"More and more often in my dreams
My faithful knight I see,
Holding the fire, he gallops up,
But I wake, and gone is he!"

"Be patient, daughter, he will come!
In seeking for the fire
He who goes after it himself
May oftentime expire."

Again the years go rolling by.
The princess waits in vain.
The horsemen never came in sight
On the mountains or the plain.

"Oh, Father dear, I fade with grief,
Sorrow burns my soul.
Can it be there is no such fire
In the world at all?"

But nothing could the mournful king
To his dear child reply.
Black doubt besieged his hoary head
And sorely did he sigh.

IV

Year after year sped past again.
His daughter watched in vain
The melancholy neighborhood:
No horse nor rider came.

At last the princess lost all hope,
And sad tears did she weep,
And soon the castle lay beneath
A lake both vast and deep.

The princess vanished in the lake
Whose source was her sweet eyes;
Since then among the mountains tall
Clear as a tear it lies.

Beneath the lake's transparent waves,
In the shadowy, green deeps,
The castle of the luckless king
Its haughty look still keeps.

And now, as soon as twilight falls
And windows come alight,
A myriad moths as if possessed
Begin their nightly flight.

And people say those luckless moths
That perish in the flame,
Were once Parvana's gallant knights
Whom passion made insane.

Turned into moths upon their way,
Whenever they see fire
They fly to it from far and near
And in the flame expire.

1902

THE CAPTURE OF FORT TEMUK

Prologue

Come hither, poor and gentle folk,
Lend an ear and listen well.
A wandering bard from distant parts,
A wondrous tale will I tell.

We are all but guests in this mortal world
Since the day we get our birth,
We come and go, each in his turn
To and from this fleeting earth.

Both love and laughter must disappear,
As will beauty, treasure and throne.
Death is for us, we are for death,
Man's work is immortal alone.

Only noble deeds will never die
Through the centuries gloried and famed.
Happy the man who through his deeds
Wins an immortal name.

Yet the evil-doer lives too without end,
Cursed be his baneful deed,
Be it your father, mother or son
Or the woman you love and need!

I sing my praise to the deed benign;
Unthrone it, whoever can!
For who, even foes, will not admire
The deeds of a kindly man?

I wish you all the best of luck!
Now listen to what I tell;
Watch my word like a bullet fly,
Shot by a hunter aiming well.

I

Nadir, the Shah, mustered his troops,
Soldiers in countless hosts;
And he beleaguered Temuk Fort,
Like a night full of fiends and ghosts.

"Hey, brave Tatul!" the Shah called out,
"You think you will never die?
Come! For it is your death I have brought,
While you on your soft bed lie."

"Do not swagger, boastful Nadir!"
Cried the giant in reply.
"A mountain will never bow its peak,
Though the blackest clouds sweep by."

He called his warriors, daring and bold,
He buckled his shining sword,
Then sprang and mounted his charger swift
And rode afield from the Fort.

For forty days and for forty nights
The battle raged without cease;
So many corpses remained from the fight,
They topped the Fort in their heaps.

Iran and Turan had all arrived,
Yet they couldn't conquer the giant.
Army, slingshots were all destroyed,
But the fortress still stood, defiant.

Back to the Fort at last he came,
Victorious, on the morn,
The dark-eyed beauty, his youthful wife,
Awaiting his return.

II

If ever a minstrel,
I swear by my soul,
A woman like that could boast,
Without any weapon
Or army he could
March against any shah's host.

Whenever they smile,
Those lovely eyes,
Fountains of love and fire,
The night becomes bright
As broad daylight
And banished are gloom and ire.

If they wish you victory,
Rose-petal lips,
When you come the foe to meet,
Then no Shah Nadir
Nor death, nor fear,
No army your might can beat.

III

On the field of battle, before the Shah,
The woman's beauty was praised.
The loveliest houri in all Iran
Could not equal her charm and grace.
This daughter of Javakh had eyes like the sea:
Men sank and were lost in her gaze.

46

Her forehead was whiter than any snow
That the lofty Abul displays.

She was Prince Tatul's living breath and soul;
The hero was drunk with her love.
He drew his might from her winning smile;
The lion gained power from the dove.
If the great Shah, could win over her heart,
Tatul, powerless, would be at his feet,
Then with ease he could capture Temuk Fort,
Which so long had withstood defeat.

IV

Here is how the immortal Farsi Firdousi,
The sweet nightingale, once opined;
Who in the world a hero could crush
        If not for women
        And wine?
With his radiant, sun-like face he stands
Like a mountain, proud and fine.
Who could level him with the ground
        If not for women
        And wine?
As if he were dancing, he goes to the fray,
As on wings he seems to fly.
Who could bring him down from his soaring flight
        If not for women
        And wine?
If even the whole world fell upon him
He would thwart the evil design.
Rustam Zal himself could not conquer him
        If not for women
        and wine?

V

So the Shah dispatched his beloved bard:
"Go, see her and ask her health.
Sing my love," he said, "to the lady fair,
Tell her of my glory and wealth."

"Promise to her my throne of gold,
Promise all that she ever desired.
Promise whatever a shah can pledge
To his lady-love or his bride."

Where the Shah could not enter by cunning or force
They welcome the bard with his saz.
So one day a minstrel, old and poor,
Through the gates of Temuk did pass.

VI

The walls of Temuk they trembled and shook
As Tatul stood against the Shah;
As foes dealt foes the most terrible blows,
Blood flowed like a sea, wide and far.

As foes dealt foes the most terrible blows,
Blood flowed like a sea, wide and far,
The minstrel sang of the glory and wealth
And the boundless love of his Shah.

While the lady fair of Temuk did attend
With secret shame she quailed,
Torn apart by temptation dire
Which to defeat she failed.

"Do you hear me, O lady fair of this Fort,
Charming beyond compare?
Look at the Shah; of his boundless might,
Of his wealth are you aware?"

"Yet like us, he too, is a frail, weak man,
Which a beauty may captive take.
A jewelled crown would befit your brow,
A majestic queen would you make...."

The lady fair of Temuk did attend
All of a night and a day....
She grew silent, meditative and pale,
And her sleep did flee away.

VII

Home from the battle came Prince Tatul,
Victorious, with his troop.
He wiped his sword, put it back in its sheath,
And the Fort shook with joy to its roof.

His lovely mistress put up a great feast,
Turned dark night into sunlit day.
The wines they flowed like a welling tide
As her lord whiled the night away.

The flower-like lady she moved about
And table by table did pass.
She bade them be merry and of good cheer
And left empty no goblet or glass.

"Raise your goblets, my valiant guests,
And here's to my brave Tatul.
God bless both him and his saber sharp,
Whose triumph was fast and full!"

"O Gracious God, make sharper the sword
Of our brave Tatul! May his land
Ever be shielded from enemies
By the power of his bounteous hand."

And it echoed and shook, did Fort Temuk,
With joyous festivity,
It thundered with the triumphant songs
And resounded with manly glee.

"Is it an eagle swooping down
From the gloomy clouds like an arrow?"
"No, 'tis Tatul from Fort Temuk
Striking fear into enemy marrow."

"Is it a dark cloud or lightning dread
Rumbling in Temuk dale?"
"No, 'tis Tatul fighting his foes,
And his sword that makes them pale."

"What mountain eagle can equal Tatul?
What shah can oppose his sword?"
And neither did wine ever cease to flow
Nor the songs in praise of their lord.
To the flower-like beauty that bloomed on their rocks
Toasts like thunder were roared.

They drank to the glory of fighting men
Shedding blood for their country's love;
To the memory of their fallen friends
Now looking at them from above.

The flower-like lady she moved about
And table by table did pass.
She bade them be merry and of good cheer,
And left empty no goblet or glass.

"O Hostess Dear, upon our word,
We can surely drink no more.
Forsooth, we have drunk and eaten our full,
Well pleased, yet tired are we sore."

Then silence fell, and in darkness wrapped
Peace came on Temuk Fort.
Drunk and fatigued, in the darkness they lay,
Fast asleep, both army and lord.

VIII

Then sinister dreams came, flock after flock,
Hovering on black wings,
Over the people, slumbering, tired,
Motionless as dead things.

And Prince Tatul had a nightmare too:
A dragon crept up to the Fort,
And coiled around it in ugly rings
As if in some awesome sport.

The monster raised its terrible head,
Up and up, ever higher,
Till it reached the chamber of Prince Tatul,
Breathing thunder and spitting fire.

And Prince Tatul he was lying in bed.
On his breast lay his wife's sweet head.
And he said to her: "My angel, get up,
And I'll strike that monster dead."

So said Prince Tatul, and suddenly saw
It was not his wife's fair head,
But the ugly head of the monster that lay
On his chest as he slept in bed.

IX

Awake, and shake off the fetters of sleep,
You brave soldiers of Prince Tatul!

Whose shadow lurks in the darkness there
As if he can't sleep his full?

Perhaps the vanquished and desperate foe
Beaten in honest fight,
Has gotten into the Fort by stealth
Plotting evil at dead of night?

Wake up, arise, for all through the night
Gaunt shapes are prowling around.
Wake, lion-like men, Tatul's brave guard,
Strike the enemy down to the ground!

Awake, get up, for the lady fair
Made you drunk and opened the gate.
The traitress has let the enemy in
And woeful is your fate....

Treason! Arise and sound the alarm!
To arms, to horse, brave men!
The gates of the castle are rolling back,
The enemy's pouring in.

X

The sun rose bright, the day was clear,
As it opened its shining eyes.
O'er the ruined Fort in a darksome cloud
Smoke and dust did rise.

The lord of the Fort and his soldiers all,
Drunk with victory and with wine,
The lord and his army, forever slept
Nor with pain and remorse did pine.

The Shah sat still and before him saw
Festive tables, abandoned and lone,
And thoughts of Man's frailty came to him
At the sight of the orphaned throne.

There is nothing secure in the universe,
Never believe in aught,
Neither luck, nor glory, nor victory,
Nor the glass by a loving wife brought....

And the awe-stricken Shah he questioned the pale
Mistress as there she stood:
"O dark-eyed traitress, come, answer me,
Was Tatul not brave and good?"

"He was far more brave and handsome than you,
He was fearless, noble and tall.
He never took castles by foul deceit,
Never so low would he fall."

The lady's answer was honest and true,
And his hangman the Shah did call:
He roared with wrath like a savage beast,
Till all rang in the spacious hall.

XI

The hangman came in, clad from head to foot
In red, at which none can look,
And led away through the castle gates
The fair lady of Fort Temuk.

She was taken away to the giant rock
That still stands in its place today,
And they threw her down in a bottomless gorge
And motionless there she lay.

And wolves and foxes came in from the plains
And devoured her base heart with wild cries;
Kites and ravens flew down from the clouds
And tore out her treacherous eyes.

So the lovely lady of Fort Temuk
Passed from the world away
Like the choicest flower of last year's spring
That will never blossom again.

And so did the dread and mighty Shah
And his army pass away too,
As did Tatul the victorious Prince,
As also will I and you.

And only this true and woeful tale
Has remained until our day,
Outlasting castles, outliving forts,
Defying death and decay.

XII

Come hither, all you good people,
Sit down and listen well.
A wandering bard from distant parts
A wondrous tale will I tell.

We all are guests in this mortal world
From the day we get our birth.
We come and go, each in his turn,
To and from this fleeting earth.

We pass away, and only our deeds
Good or bad, live on in fame.
So blessed be he who leaves the world
As pure a man as he came.

Sculpture of David of Sassoun in Yerevan, Armenia by the famous Sculptor Yervant Kochar

DAVID OF SASSOUN

I

Lion-Mher of fabled glory
For forty years at Sassoun reigned;
He reigned with might, and in his day
No flocks made flight o'er Sassoun's steeps.
Far and away from Sassoun highlands
His mighty name was rumored wide;
His name bespoke his valor, his fearsome deeds—
The single name, Lion-Mher.

II

Thus, seated like a fearful lion
In the Sassoun fastnesses, he had reigned
As lord for forty years. For forty years
He had never raised a wail of woe;
But now, fallen upon declining days,
Into that fearless heart there crept a sting.
Thus the legend-laden man to thinking fell;
"Alack, the autumn days of my life are come,
The black earth soon will claim me for its own,
Like smoke will pass the glories of Lion-Mher,
Even my name, terror and fear;
Alas! On my unowned and orphaned realm
There rise a thousand upstart braves and fiends....
Upon my passing, alack, no heir remains
To buckle on my sword, protector be to Sassoun....
Pondered thus the troubled childless grey-beard.

III

Thus on a day, his iron-grey eyebrows knitted,
Deep he pondered, when down from the sky,
Fronting the giant, stood a fiery angel,
His feet enwrapped in billowing clouds.
"Greetings! All-powerful giant of Sassoun,
Your voice has reached the throne of God;
Soon he shall grant to you a child.
But harken well, O lord of the Mountains,
On that day, when God grants you an heir,
On that selfsame day will you and your wife die."
"His will be done," spake Lion-Mher, "we are ever
Of death and death of us; but if of this world
We gain an heir, with him deathless we remain."
Here the fiery angel once more took aloft;
And onward from that happy day of joyous tidings,
When nine months did pass and nine hours more,
Lion-Mher a child did have; and David
He named his cub, and called to him his brother,
Big-Voiced Ohan: bequeathed his lands and scion
To him. That day died he and his dame, too.

IV

And in those times in Egypt there sat a king,
Melik of Musr, mighty and unvanquished;
When he heard that Lion-Mher no more was,
Straight upon Sassoun he marched to fight.
Ohan the Big-Voiced, set a-quake with fear, came before
The war-like hosts unhelmeted and bowed,
And seeking mercy, fell upon his knees.
"O Melik be you the master of our heads,"
He said, "while beneath your shadow we live;
Ever may we your servants be, our tribute pay,
Only lay not waste our tillage and our lands,
And with benign ear hark you to us."

"Nay," roared Melik, "your people all must pass
Beneath my sword and homage pay, so that
Henceforth whatever I will to do, not one
Sassounite may raise a sword against me."
Thus Ohan went and brought all Sassounites
Together and passed them all beneath the sword;
David alone, despite whatever moves
Were tried, came not near the foeman Melik's sword.
Vexed, the Sassounites came and tugged at him:
He bolted once, scattered the throng here and there,
The while his little finger grazed a rock
And drew from it a flight of fiery bolts.
To the wise men gathered all about him,
Spoke the King: "I must kill this little fool!"
"O King," they said, "beneath your sword today
All Sassoun stands; sure you are the mighty one.
What is there a mere child could do against thee,
Though he were instead altogether fire?"
"You know best," said the Egyptian king, "but if,
On a day some harm should fall upon my head,
This day be witness,
From him will it come."

V

When this event occurred our husky David
A mere child was, seven or eight years old.
I say a child, but for one with so much strength,
Man and mosquito were the same.
But, alas for the poor orphan on this earth,
Though he come forth from the loins of a lion!
Now Big-Voiced Ohan had a waspish wife;
Once or twice she held her tongue, but one day
Thus she began fighting with her helpmeet:
"A lonely soul I, heir to a thousand ills,
Why have you brought another's orphan here,

Weighed me down with a useless trencherman....
Would that I could cast sod upon his head!
No handmaid I, dancing attendance upon others!
Find a way to lose him, put him to a task,
Pack him off that he may labor for himself."
Saying thus, she began to wail and weep,
To mourn her hapless days, to curse her fate,
That luckless she was to be on earth,
That nor master her did own, nor pitying spouse.
Ohan set out and brought back a pair
Of iron boots for the feet of the child,
Placed an iron staff upon his shoulders,
And made him the shepherd of Sassoun-town.

VI

The mighty shepherd drove his flock of sheep
And mounted Sassoun's peerless fastnesses:
>   "O endearing highlands,
>   Highlands of Sassoun...."
When he called, of such force was his voice,
That canyons and highlands sounded with it,
Wild animals sprang from their lairs, scattered
From rock to rock, and became homeless.
David went after them all, those from the valleys,
And those from the hills—fox, hare, wolf, and deer
He gathered and brought and mixed with his flock,
And at night drove them all on Sassoun-town.
The noise and the din, the sounds and the roars,
The charging of numberless beasts let loose,
The townspeople suddenly saw and heard.
>   "Oh! Help! Run...."
>   Old and young,
>   Panic-stricken,
>   Away did run
>   From their chores.

Some ran home, some to church, some to shops.
All bolted doors fast and closed shutters tight.
Boldly David strode and stood in the town square—
      How early these people are gone to sleep!
      Ho there, goat-owners, sheep-owners!
      Get up, swiftly unbar your doors!
      He who had one—I've brought him ten,
      He who had ten—I've brought him scores.
      Up, get up swiftly, come and take them,
      Take your sheep and your goats to the barns."
When David saw that no one stirred, no one
A door unbarred, he placed his head upon
A stone, lengthened himself out upon the square,
And soundly slept until the break of dawn.
At dawn the nobles arose together
And went to Big-Voiced Ohan and said:
"Thou Big-Voiced Ohan, be thou taken by Death!
You it was who brought this fool, made him herdsman.
He parts nor sheep nor wolves nor foxes,
Thus with wild beasts has he filled our town.
If lovest thou God, put him to another task,
Else he'll burst the galls of all our townsfolk."

VII

Ohan arose and went to see David.
"Uncle Ohan, take care, tread softly,
Else the goats will scamper off." And hard by
An ash-colored hare, its ears fixed rigid,
Affrighted became and bolted away.
David was up in a trice and after it.
In the hills he caught the hare and brought it back
And placed it once again among the goats.
"Oh, how hard it is, Uncle Ohan. . . .
God has blessed those black-black goats, but
    these that be

Ash-colored goats, are ever escaping
And ever scattering into the hills.
So much did I scurry yesterday,
Until I gathered them and brought them back.
Ohan saw that David's boots were not what
They were, his goatherd's staff worn to the butt,
So much in a single day had he run.
"David, my soul, I cannot leave thee thus,
The ash-colored goats are torturing you.
Tomorrow take the flocks to the pasture,"
Ohan said. And the next morning he went
And brought still another pair of iron boots
For David's feet, and brought an iron staff
A hundred pounds in weight, and made David
The pasture-keeper of Sassoun-town.

VIII

The mighty shepherd drove his herd of cattle
And mounted Sassoun's peerless fastnesses:

> "O endearing highlands,
> Highlands of Sassoun,
> How sweet the slopes rise
> Against thy rock-ribbed sides...."

When David sang, of such force was his voice
That canyons and highlands sounded with it,
Wild beasts from their lairs sprang forth and scattered
From rock to rock, became homeless. David
Fell after them all, those from the valleys,
Those from the hills—wolf, leopard, lion, bear, tiger
He caught and brought and mixed with his herd,
And at night drove them all on Sassoun-town.
The noise and the din, the sounds and the roars,
The charging of numberless beasts let loose,
The townspeople suddenly heard and saw....

"Oh! Help! Run...."
Old and young,
Panic-stricken,
Away did run
From their chores.

Some ran home, some to church, and some to shops,
All bolted doors fast and closed shutters tight.
Boldly David strode and in the town square stood....
"Well, how early these people are gone to sleep!

Ho there, oxen-owners, cow-owners!
Get up, swiftly unbar your doors!
He who had one—I've brought him ten,
He who had ten—I've brought him scores.
Up, get up swiftly, come and take them,
Take your oxen and your cows to the barns."

When David saw that no one stirred, no one
The doors unbarred, he placed his head upon
A stone, himself lengthened out upon the square,
And soundly slept until the break of dawn.
At dawn the nobles arose together
And went to Ohan the Big-Voiced, and said:
"Big-Voiced brother Ohan, alas, Death take you!
You it was who brought this fool, made him herdsman.
Our cows and our oxen, unshepherded
Let them be, but rid us of this madcap lout.
He parts nor bear nor ram nor ox;
Some day he'll bring great harm upon our town,
Make it a lair for bears, a forsaken land."

IX

A nuisance David! No peace from the lad!
Put to it, and to his wit's end driven,
Ohan fashioned and to David gave
Bow and arrows. "Go you forth, hunt among the hills."

From Ohan David took the bow and arrows,
Went forth beyond the bounds of Sassoun-town.
Huntsman he became. Into a barley field
He sallied forth, killing quail, shooting sparrow.
And at dusk, he took haven in a hut
Cared for by a poor and childless woman,
Betimes to his father known. There, alongside
The fire, like an immense and long dragon,
He would lengthen himself out and sleep.
On a day, when he was from the hunt returned,
This woman raged at him. "Goodness, David!" she said,
"Death take you! Are you indeed your father's son?
That field alone and I remain below
The skies and God. An old lady I, weak
Of hand and foot—Why do you trample
My field under foot, and lay it waste,
Cut off my whole year's living? If you are a
Huntsman, take up your bow and arrows—betake
You to the headlands of Zudsmaga, all
The way to Seghansar—your sire held there
Of an entire domain the tenancy.
Well-stocked are its highlands with roaming game;
There are deer there, mountain-goat and wild sheep.
If you can, begone, go seek your game there."
"What is it, you hag, that makes you curse me?
Still a stripling I, now only have I heard.
Where be then the fastness of our game preserve?"
"To your uncle go, Ohan will tell it thee."

X

Next day at sunrise David stood before
His uncle's threshold with bow in hand.
"Uncle Ohan, why have you not told me
My father owned a mountain game preserve?
There are mountain goats there, rams and deer.

Up, Uncle, bestir yourself and take me there."
"What!" cried Ohan, "These are not your words.
Whoso told them you, may his tongue be tied!
That mountain game preserve, my son, is lost
To us, as also the game of that range. . . .
No more are there mountain goats, rams, deer.
In the days when your father was still quick
(O what wondrous days, whence are ye fled?)
Oft have I eaten there the flesh of game. . . .
Your father died, God forsook us, Egypt's king
Gathered soldiers, came upon us, ruined
Our country, and the game from this mountain
He took, he plundered: the deer, the hind are gone. . . .
Hence our fate's scroll has thus been written.
All is past, my son, go back to your work,
The king of Egypt else will hear your voice."
"What can the king of Egypt do to me?
What do I ask from the king of Egypt?
Let the king of Egypt stay in Egypt.
To my father's highlands what right has he?
Up, Uncle, take up your bow and arrows,
Your quiver buckle on, to the highlands
Let us go, to the mountain game preserve!"
Ohan stood up, not knowing what to do.
They went, and what a game preserve they saw!
The high walls demolished, thick forests felled,
The high turrets made level with the earth.

XI

Night fell and there they remained fast.
Big-Voiced Ohan placed beneath his head the quiver
And the bow and peacefully snored. David
Was plunged into a sea of reckonings.
And soon he saw, in the distant darkness,
A strong and flaming fire burning bright.

Toward the fire David moved, and held by
Its spell, straightway was borne upward upon it.
Upward and upward he went, alighted on
A rock, ascended again, saw a great
Cleft marble stone, from its center belching forth
A pure flame, rising and falling, billow
Upon billow, on the selfsame stone.
Now David came down from the place, came down
And called Big-Voiced Ohan. "Up, Uncle, up
And see that bright fire burning brightly there.
How long will you sleep! A light has come down
From the steep hill, the steep hill of marble stone.
Arise, Uncle, from your sweet sleep! What light
Is that that issues forth from your marble stone?"
Ohan stood up and made the sign of the cross
Against his face. "Alas, my son," he said,
"How I cherish that light! That is the light
From our great peak Marouta. In the place
Of that light there once did stand our Sassoun's
Patroness (What wondrous days!), Sassoun's guardian,
The blessed Madonna's monastery
Of Charghopan. Always, when to war he went,
It was there your father made his prayers.
Your father died, God was wroth and forsook us,
The king of Egypt gathered up soldiers,
He marched upon our abbey on that hill,
He levelled it, but from the altar still
The sacred flames of our patroness rise."

XII

When David heard this, "Sweet Uncle," he said,
"Uncle sweet, orphan and liegeless I am
In this world, because I lack a father, be you
To me a father good. I'll not again
From Marouta's heights come down until

Once again our abbey stands as it used to.
From you I ask five hundred artisans,
Five thousand toilers, too, with them to work
So that this very week they come and build
Our former abbey as it erewhile stood."
Now Ohan went forth and with him brought back
Five thousand toilers, five hundred artisans,
Who, mid sound and fury, builded again,
Much as before with glories overlaid,
Our Blessed Mary's abbey, Marouta.
The scattered clergy once again came back,
And once again the sound of canticle
And prayer re-echoed through the abbey's walls.
When once again his father's monastery
Full-peopled was and merry, David came down,
And only then came he, from Marouta's heights.

XIII

This news was taken to Egypt's Melik.
"Well, don't tell me! So David has rebuilt
His father's abbey and become the ruler,
While I have yet the seven years' tribute to
Collect!" Now Melik was exceeding wroth:
"Go," he said, "Patin, Gouzpatin, Sitvin,
Charghatin, Sassoun's earth and stones lay waste.
To me bring back my seven years' tribute rich.
Bring forty virgin girls, nimbus-lit,
Forty short women to turn the millstones,
And forty tall to load the camel trains,
To be at beck and call my household slaves."
Gouzpatin marshalled up his soldiers true,
"Gladly, my Lord," he said, "so be it.
I go to Sassoun even now to lay
It bare, to bring back groups of forty women,
Forty camel-loads of yellow gold,

And ruin the home of the Armenian race."
Thus he spoke. Egyptian maids and women
Together danced and raised their voice in song:
"Our Gouzpatin has to Sassoun gone. . . .
Groups of forty women have I brought,
Forty saddle bags of gold,
Before my eyes in serried order
Have I brought milch-cows red. . . .
In the springtime let us butter churn,
O Gouzpatin, brave Gouzpatin,
Cast is David in the dust."
Now Gouzpatin, swollen with pride, roaring said,
"I thank you sisters all, but patient be
Till I return—it's then that you should dance."

XIV

Thus with a song,
With soldiers strong
Haughty Gouzpatin entered Sassoun.
Straight when Ohan heard this he was tongue-tied:
With salt and bread,
With cries and tears,
He bowed his head
Before the spears,
For mercy prayed.
"Have whatever you wish, so be it; take
Rosy-cheeked girls, of Sassoun-town the womenfolk,
The yellow gold that's hard come by, take these,
Take these but mercy show our hapless race.
Do not cut us down nor do us in to death,
Above is God, below are you," he said.
He brought row on row of rosy-cheeked girls
And womenfolk of Sassoun-town. Up stood
Gouzpatin and gleaned; he lodged the likelier of them
Deep within the hayloft and locked the door. . . .

Forty virgin girls beauteously nimbus-lit,
Forty short women to turn the millstones,
And forty tall to load the camel-trains,
To be household slaves of Egypt's Melik.
And from its hold mound on mound of yellow gold....
A pall of mourning hung on the Armenian race.

XV

Where are you, O David, you guardian of
The Armenian race, O let the rock be rent,
Only come you out into the open!
Once David had repaired the abbey of
His sires, he dropped down from Marouta's peak,
He found a tarnished, helveless blade and stepped
Into the grandam's turnip field. The hag
Came forth with cries and curses. "Fool David,"
She said, "may you one day eat fire and pain
Instead of turnips. In this wide world
Do your eyes see only me and what are mine?
My field you've levelled to the ground, you have,
This only had remained my winter's hoard,
This too have you cut off; how shall I live?
If you be brave, take your bow, begone,
Hold sway over your father's domains,
Eat from the treasures of your father
Which you have so long unprotected left
That Egypt's king has sent to pack them off."
"Why are you so angered with me, grandam?
I know not a thing of what you say.
What is it that Egypt's king takes from us?"
"The Egyptian king, heavy-footed David,
Gouges your very eyes: already is
He here. On Sassoun-town have come Patin,
Gouzpatin, Sitvin, Charghatin; the whole
Of Sassoun-town they plunder even now...

Forty saddle-bags of gold for tribute,
Forty beauteous virgin girls, nimbus-lit,
Forty short women to turn the millstones,
Forty tall women to load the camel-trains,
All to be slaves to the Egyptian king."
"O grandam why do you curse me? But show
And let me see—These demands, where are they made?"
"Death take you David! 'Where are they made!'
Are you really the son of that father,
You who are come here to munch on turnips?
In your very house Gouzpatin measures
Out your gold, while the pretty girls
Are together herded in your hayloft."
David left off eating turnips and went.
He spied Gouzpatin in his home, counting
The gold before him spilled, and Charghatin
And Sitvin holding back the barking dogs,
While at a distance, his neck to one side bent,
His arms folded across his breast, Ohan stood.
David saw, and his eyes were gorged with blood.
"Stop! Gouzpatin, stand apart! This is my father's gold!
I am the one to count it out."
Gouzpatin said: "Well, Big-Voiced Ohan,
This seven years' tribute will you give or not?
If not, may my whiskers witness be, I'll leave
And tell Musra-Melik, and he will come,
He will lay waste your Sassoun countryside,
Burn it down and plant a garden over it."
"Begone, you unfeeling Egyptian dogs!
Have you yet to hear of Sassoun's mighty braves?
Think you we are dead, or mere shadows all?
Think you to place our country under tribute?"
David's wrath was great. At once he clapped
The weighing scales, which smashed Gouzpatin's head.
Their fragments flew beyond the walls: Till now,
To this very day, still are they in flight. . . .

Now they rose up, let be the scattered gold,
Left far behind the Armenian world and fled—
Patin, Gouzpatin, Sitvin, Charghatin.

XVI

"Well, well, Uncle, what shall I say to you?
We have here mound on mound of gold.
Of me a servant of the town you've made,
Abandoned me before an alien's door."
"You crazy fool," his uncle said, "I've kept
For Melik all this gold that he might kindly
Look upon us. Now that you gave it not,
Who is there will front his wroth, fight with him,
When he comes forth with soldiers and with fire
To lay in ruins Sassoun's earth and stones?"
"Stay, Uncle, let him come forth, I shall go,
I shall go forth and answer to him make."
He smote the door against the dark hayloft,
Let out the pinioned girls and set them free.
"Go," he said, "in freedom live, and fail not
To pray long days for David of Sassoun."

XVII

So, battered in this way and bathed in blood,
Homeward-bound they fled and reached their
        native land,

        Patin, Gouzpatin,
        Sitvin, Charghatin.

Egyptian women saw them in the distance,
Saw them in the distance and were right glad....
From the rooftops they clapped and cheered
        them home.
            "They come, they come...
            They bear, they bear.

Our Gouzpatin has come from Sassoun-town,
Brought back groups of forty women,
And red milch cows.
In the spring we'll butter make and chortaan."

But once they saw at closer range
Gouzpatin bloodied,
They ceased giggling and wagged aloud:
"Well Gouzpatin, you loud-mouthed runaway,
Down what dales and over what mountain have
    you fled,
Your thick head cleft in half? Did you not say,
'To Sassoun I go to fetch groups of forty women,
To fetch forty saddle-bags of yellow gold,
To lay waste the country of the Armenian race?'
As a breathless, fleeing hound have you returned!"
Gouzpatin, now angered much, began to speak:
"Silence, you brats, you've seen only your breed
Of men and not the mighty Sassoun braves.
Sassoun's mighty braves are mountain-like,
Their arrows thick as stakes, and their country
Withal a stony fastness: canyon-walls,
Impenetrable, abound and deep hollows.
Even their blades of grass stand curved as swords.
They slaughtered three hundred men, Egypt's best."
Thus he spoke and, once he had, he tarried not,
But ran fast, head over heels, pell-mell,
Ran right up to the king. The king laughed from
His throne. "Live, O live, brave Gouzpatin!
The famed medallion of Ghouzghoun richly
You deserve, and from your neck shall it hang,
A guerdon for your great triumphal stroke.
But where are they? Bring Sassoun's girls and gold."
Thus Melik spoke; but Gouzpatin had bowed
His head clear to the very ground. He said:
"Live long, O great king! Barely did I flee,

71

Though mounted on my horse. How could I
Have borne Sassoun's yellow gold? A fool is
Born among the Armenian race who brooks nor
Lord nor fear nor mighty men. See how he's
Had at my bloodied head and smashed it through.
'I will not give,' he said, 'my father's gold.
Nor will I give the womenfolk of my
Armenian people. In Sassoun-country
There is no room for you. Your king,' he said,
'Let him come, let him come and fight with me.
If brave he be, let him come and take by force.' "
The Egyptian king, enraged, boiled over and over.
"Call," he said, "call all my soldiers together:
A thousand males, young recruits,
A thousand thousand males, beardless, without
    moustache,
A thousand thousand males, downy-lipped,
A thousand thousand males, fresh from the couch,
A thousand thousand males, black-moustachioed,
A thousand thousand males, grey-haired,
A thousand thousand males to sound trumpets,
A thousand thousand males to strike the war-drums,
Have them come forth, take up arms, get into mail—
I go to wage war on David, desolate
Sassoun-town and plunder it to the ground."

XVIII

Thus he assembled an innumerable
Host, marched on the plains of Sassoun and encamped
In full solemnity, did the Egyptian king.
So great a population did they make
That those who came to Batman's banks bent down
And drank their fill till the river went dry,
And Sassoun's townspeople were parched with thirst.
Big-Voiced Ohan was taken by surprise.

His fur-skin on his shoulders, he scaled the heights,
He scaled the heights, and, lo, what a sight he saw:
The white tents had so whitened all the plains
That one might say mid-winter night had come,
And with white snow had covered Sassoun-town.
His gall to water turned, his tongue stood tied,
And shouting his wonder he rushed back home.
"Run, for heaven's sake, run, it's come, it's come!"
"What, Uncle, what? What has come? Who has come?"
(Fell fire-and-pain has come to David's nose.)
"Egypt's king has risen and come, come and pitched
His tented armies on our plain. The stars
May be numbered but not his numberless hosts.
Alas, for our lives, alas for our world!
Come, let us take the gold, let us take the girls,
Let us fall on the ground before him, say prayers,
Perchance he may relent, forbear the sword."
"Stay, Uncle, be not afraid; get you to
Your restful room and sleep on peacefully.
But now I'll get up, gain the Sassoun plain
And make answer to the Egyptian king."
Straight went David to his wonted grandam.
"Granny, my soul," he said, "give me some scraps
Of iron, tarnished and old, a grate, a spit.
Gather whatever you can and give it to me.
Also find me an ass on which I may sit.
Against the Egyptian hosts I go to war."
"My goodness, David," she said, "Death take you!
Can you indeed be the son of that sire?
Your father had in war a fiery steed,
Fully caparisoned, with a bellyband of gold;
A club of steel, a pearled saddle, helmet
Hardy, and a ready cross on his right arm,
Mailed vest, and a sword lightning-laden.
And now here have you come, O you warped fool,
Asking from me an ass and an old spit."

"O granny, not yet have I heard such things.
Where is now the armor of my father?"
"Go now to your uncle, ask it of him,
Say, 'Where are they? Find, bring them, give to me.'
If willingly he gives them not to you,
Gouge his eyes," she said, "and take them forcibly."

XIX

And David went to see his uncle Ohan.
"O Uncle," he called angered, "for battle
My father had a fiery steed fully
Caparisoned, with a bellyband of gold;
A club of steel, a pearled saddle, helmet
Hardy, and a ready cross on his right arm,
Mailed vest, and a lightning-laden sword."
"Oh David, my soul," Ohan roared in fear,
"Since from the day of your father's death
I have not brought forth the steed from the barn,
Nor from the arms-chest the sword of lightning,
The mailed vest, the golden bellyband.
For goodness sake, let me be, plague me not.
If these you want, scamper off and get them."

XX

David clapped on his armor and his mail;
Buckled on, too, the belt of his lightning-sword
And, with the cross on his all-conquering arm,
Mounted his lion-hearted father's steed,
Mounted his father's steed and lashed it forth.
Weeping, Big-Voiced Ohan sang:
"Mercy, a thousand mercies
For the steed,
Alas, the fiery steed,
Mercy, a thousand mercies

For the bellyband,
Alas, the golden bellyband,
Mercy that the rich array is lost,
Alas, the rich array is lost."
David flew into a rage,
Turned his horse and drove it back;
Poor Ohan paled, stood sore afraid,
And changed the burden of his song:
"Alas, my infant David's lost,
Alas, my David's lost...."
This when David heard,
His temper cooled—
He dismounted and kissed Ohan's hand;
And Big-Voiced Ohan, as a father should,
Blessed him and gave him paternal counsels,
And put him on the road to Sassoun plain.

XXI

Now, David of Sassoun an uncle had—
Toros by name—a fearful, giant-like man.
When he, too, heard of the rumors of war,
With an elm-tree on his shoulder he strode forth.
From afar he comes; roaring aloud he cries:
"Why are you come upon this field? Who are you,
How many heads may there be among you?
Have you no knowledge of David of Sassoun,
Have you not heard he's on his way here,
And brings his winged horse to pace him around?
Clear away, David will be coming here,
Wherever he is—I've come to make a clearing.

As thus he spoke, he brought the elm-tree down
From his shoulder and swept off some twenty
Pitched tents of the army, the while David stood
On a fearsome height and roared a dragon's roar.

"You who are asleep, wake up,
You who are awake, get up and stand,
You who are afoot, take arms,
You who are armed, saddle your horses,
You who are saddled, mount your horses—
That you may not later say that while asleep
David stole stealthily upon you and left...."

Thus he roared, and goading his fiery steed,
Came down like a lightning-bolt as from a cloud,
Spread terror among the Egyptian armies,
On all sides brandishing his lightning-sword.

He smashed and slew and slaughtered till high noon,
At high noon the blood rose in a floodtide;
He rounded up and drove off together
Thousands among those quick, among those dead.
Among the soldiers was an ancient man,
A sage, and one well-travelled in this world.
"Men," he said, "make way for me, make way,
I must go to David and with him speak."

He went to David and stood before him;
And this is how the elder spoke to him:
"O brave one, may your fist stay ever strong,
And in your hand always the stubby sword.

"But listen to the words of an old man
And see if there be any sense to them.
Pray tell, what have these men done unto you
That drives you on pell-mell to slaughter them?

"Each one among them is a mother's son,
And each one a burning light in his home.
Far behind some have left their forlorn wives,
Wives whose eyes look on the road for their return.

"Some have left a home with many children filled,
Some have left behind parents old and poor,
And some in tears, with veils across their faces,
Are you the young brides of only yesterday.

"Under sway of sword and by might, their king has
Gathered them up and marched them here together.
We are men to be pitied, with hastening days.
What harm have we brought to you, in what ways?

"Your foe's the warring king, the king himself,
If you must fight, go fight with him instead.
Pray leave off drawing your lightning-laden sword,
Spare these people—helpless, unprotected."

"You speak right well and true, O ancient man,"
Said David to his uncle. "But where is the
Warring king? What can he now be doing?
Bring him forth that I may wreathe his days in black."

"He has sent out from the great-tent, the one
That has the smoke issuing forth from its center;
Yonder smoke is not smoke rising to the sky,
It is vapor from the king's fuming mouth."

Thus they spoke. Now David goaded on his
Horse and rode straight to where the great-tent stood.
He rode, and rode up to the entrance-door.
Thus he roared upon the Arabs standing guard:

"Where is he?" he said. "Why has be become scarce?
Call him out, into the open call him out;
If he knows not death, I have brought him death,
If he knows not his nemesis, she am I."

"Melik," they said, "has fallen asleep."
For seven days must he sleep. Three days only

Have yet passed, four days more there now
Remain ere he will have had his share of sleep."

"What! Has he brought these poor and pitiful folk,
Dumped them on this field, spilled their blood in seas,
While he seeks shelter under cover of
His great-tent, and sleeps peacefully for seven days!

"I cannot abide whether he sleeps or no.
Quick! Get him up and out into the open;
In such wise I'll put him to sleep before
His entrance-door, he'll never again awake."

The men arose, crestfallen, then heated
An iron rod on the fire; they rapped upon
The open heels of the Egyptian king
Who was sunk in a deep peaceful sleep.

"How now! A body can no longer have
A peaceful sleep, the fleas are so noisome."
So the great husky murmured to himself,
Turned around and once more fell asleep.

They went and with a great plough they returned;
In the strong and burning fire they placed its share;
And red-hot when it was, reddened and sparkling,
Straightway they clapped it on his naked back.

"How now! A body can no longer have
A peaceful sleep, mosquitoes are so unjust."
Slowly the great husky opened his eyes,
He wanted so to fall asleep again,

But David he saw. Muttering to himself,
He lifted his great head from where he slept.

A great blast of air he blew on David,
Thinking in this way to set that giant to flight.

And when he saw that David stood stock-still,
Surprise and dread struck through his very soul.
His menacing, bloodshot eyes he cast sidelong
Gloweringly at David's unblinking eyes.

But just as soon as he had looked, he felt
From him had ebbed the strength of half-score oxen.
So on the place he slept he now sat up,
And smiling, thus began to speak with him:

"Hello, well-met, David, you are still tired.
Come, sit down a bit—let's talk as is proper.
Later we may still engage in combat,
That is, if you seek another combat."

The scheming tyrant, within his great-tent
Had caused a deep pit of forty spans to be dug,
Of which the black mouth had been covered over
With a screen and, over yet that, some bright
     throw-rugs.

His was ever the habit fawningly to lure
Unto him all those he failed to vanquish;
He coaxed them to sit within his great-tent,
Directly over that black and deadly well.

Dismounting from his horse, David came down;
He went in, he sat, he fell into the well.
Ha-ha, ha-ha, ho-ho, ho-ho, ha-ha,
Laughed Egypt's merciless king, the king of Egypt.

"There, now let him go and stay in that dark
Well till he rots away and then some more."

Saying this, he brought an immense millstone,
A millstone immense, and rolled it over the well.

XXII

On that selfsame night Big-Voiced Ohan slept.
He dreamt that there appeared, up in the sky
Over Egypt, a bright sun, bright with rays,
But over Sassoun's fastnesses, a black cloud.

Ohan was terror-stricken. From his bed
He sprang. "O wife," he said, "bring up a light.
Our artless David is in trouble again,
And a black cloud hangs over Sassoun-town."

"May the sod fall on your head!" said his wife.
"Who knows how or where David's having fun.
Yet here you are asleep in your cozy home,
Seeing dreams and about others worrying."

Ohan fell asleep. Again he started up:
"O wife, David is come to narrow straits.
So brightly glimmers Egypt's brilliant star,
But sicklied over glows our star and yellow."

"What's come over you, man, in the middle of
The night?" his wife shouted in a fury.
Ohan again crossed himself upon the face,
Turned around and slept, though with a troubled heart.

He saw another dream, more fearful than
Before: from heaven's high arch there now sparkled,
Full-resplendently, Egypt's star; Sassoun's
Waning little star sank slowly, toward the dark.

He woke up, afraid: "Wife, may your house
      be wrecked!

How could I listen to your witless brains!
Alone unto himself our young and orphaned
David now is lost. Up! Bring me my arms."

XXII

Ohan arose and went forth to the barn
And gave his white horse a pat on the back.
"Well, white horse," he said, "how long will it be
For you betake me to where David fights?"

"By dawn you shall be there," and saying this,
The white horse stooped for him to mount.
"Your back be broken! What'll I do at dawn,
View his corpse or his funeral attend?"

He gave the red horse a pat on the back.
That horse, too, stooped for Ohan to mount.
"O red horse," he said, "how long will it be
Ere you betake me to where David fights?"

"In one hour you shall be there," the red horse said,
"In one hour I'll take you where David fights."
"May you burst your gall! Pain and Death take you!
Alas for all that barley you have eaten."

And now to the black horse the turn came around.
The black horse, too, stooped for him to mount.
"O my little black one, how long will it be,"
He said, "ere you take me where David fights?"

"If on my back you can stay fast," the black
Horse said, "No sooner your one foot's in the
Stirrup and before the other one's thrown over,
I will have brought you where David fights."

Swiftly the black horse bore Big-Voiced Ohan:
He placed his left foot in the stirrup,
By the time he threw his right foot over,
The black horse had brought him to the highlands.

Now Ohan saw David's steed, unmounted,
A-roaming in the highlands and neighing aloud:
Below, he saw the Egyptian encampment,
Undulating endlessly like the sea.

And that he might not burst with his straining,
Ohan put on the skins of seven oxen.
And Ohan stood, like a cloud, atop the
Topmost peak in Sassoun's highlands, and roared:

"O David, O David, where can you be!
But call to mind the cross on your arm, give
The name of our Blessed Madonna
And come you out into the broad daylight."

His voice floated, reverberatingly,
And into David's inner ear blared strong.
"Ho-ho! That is my uncle's voice," he said,
"From Sassoun's fastnesses he calls for me."

"O blessed Madonna of Marouta,
O intrepid cross of our litany,
I call on you—save our David now."
He called, and from his place rose to his feet:

In such strength, in such wise he smote the millstone,
The stone was smashed into a thousand pieces.
The pieces upward flew to high heaven,
And still to this day are they in flight.

Melik, formidable, came out of his lair;
By fear his fiendish spirit was possessed.
"Brother David, do still come over here,
Let us sit at board together and parley."

"Never again at board will I sit with you,
You base, you crooked, you poltroonly man;
Get up, quick, take up your arms, mount your horse,
Come out into the open and let us fight."

"Indeed let's fight, let us fight," Melik said,
"But mine is the right to strike the first blow."
"Oh very well, it's yours, so strike," David called.
He rode and stopped in the middle of the plain.

Musra-Melik arose, came to his feet.
He took up his lance and mounted his horse,
And dashed off all the way to Diarbekir,
And from that place yet again returned.

Three thousand boulders was Melik drawing
By the handle of his gigantic lance.
He charged and struck a blow—at once the dust
Arose and the world's globe trembled strong.

"There's been an earthquake or the world's destroyed,"
Said many people throughout the world:
"No," others said, "bloodthirsty giants,
Men of might, are having at each other."

"From but this single blow hath David died,"
Musra-Melik told his myriad soldiers,
But David from beneath a cloud called forth,
"Musra-Melik, yet am I among the quick!"

"Well, from short distance only did I charge,
But you'll see now from where it is I come!"
Arose the mighty one, came to his feet,
And sprang on his mount for a second time.

Clear to Aleppo he rode the second time,
On his way back from there he left free the reins:
Rains came and hail, and a strong hurricane
With its tremendous force, shook the whole world.

He came, he struck, and from the clamor of
The blow, standers-by were fully deafened.
"Lost is David to the House of Sassoun,"
Announced the haughty Egyptian monarch.

"Among the quick am I," shouted David,
"Charge once again—'tis still your turn."
"Well! From short distance only did I charge,"
Melik shouted, and sprang upon his mount.

The third time now that he mounted his horse,
Out and away he rode to Egypt's own soil,
And from that distance, the lance in his hand,
Back he rode, charging full-tilt on David.

He charged on David and struck with all his strength,
Struck with a crushing and formidable blow:
The dust went up as high as Sassoun's steeps,
So dense it was the sun's face stood beclouded.

For three nights and for three days, the dust lay
Like a cloud over all the countryside.
For three nights and for three days, the rumors
Went forth that David of Sassoun had died.

When there had passed three days, like the dust
That stood cloudlike, David too did stand;
Yea, as the peak, the peak of Mount Kur-Kur
Stood David, fog-shrouded and majestic.

"O Melik," he roared, "whose turn is it now?"
The proud soul of Melik was terror-stricken:
Death's tremors now possessed his very heart,
His haughty, puffed-up spirit was now let down.

Melik strode forth and dug himself a deep well,
He let himself down into the darkness below.
He covered its opening with forty skins,
And covered these again with forty millstones.

That lion-hearted son of the lion-hearted,
David, stood up from where he sat, grumbling,
Mounted his stormy steed, made it career,
As aloft he held his gleaming Lightning-Sword.

There now came forth, her hair loosed before her,
The mother of Melik, a mean old crone:
"O David, by my hair draw me beneath
Your heels, but deal thy very first blow to me."

The second time he lifted high his sword,
There came running Musra-Melik's sister:
"O David, if it be your wish," she called,
"Strike your second blow on my fainting heart."

Now the hour had come for the final blow;
And for the third time David raised his sword.
"Now one blow have I left. I must strike
    for God's sake,"
He said, "I must strike...no one else remains."

Saying thus, he mounted, careered his horse.
His fiery steed took flight and sailed high,
In the heavens careered, defiantly—
Then downward came the lightning-laden sword.

Through forty hides of oxen did it pass,
Also through forty millstones did it pass,
Clear through the loathsome monster did it cleave,
Cut into his flesh seven feet deep.

"I am among the quick! Strike once again!"
Melik roared from deep within the well.
David heard, and was much astonished
At the blow he'd struck with his Lightning-Sword.

"Melik," he said, "do move about a bit."
And Melik made a stir within the well.
Right down the middle his body split,
Once section falling here, another there.

The Egyptian soldiers, when they viewed that sight,
Terror-stricken, their blood to water turned.
David called: "Be none of you in fear,
But listen yet to what I have to say.

"You are but tillers of the soil, farmers,
Benighted and denied, hungry, naked,
With a thousand and one ills and pains,
With a thousand and one troubles to boot.

"Why have you taken up the bow and arrow,
Spilled over onto far and alien plains?
Know you not that we too have homes and hearths,
We too have tender babes and the aged?

"Have you tired of the quiet and peaceful life,
The quiet and peaceful life of the husbandman?
Are you tired of the threshing-floor, the field,
Tillage and sowing, your harvests and greens?

"Return you by the paths that brought you here,
Return to your native soil of Egypt;
But if once again by might and in arms
You should dare to march against these freeborn men,

"Be the wells you dig forty measures deep,
Be they covered up with forty millstones,
Against you will rise, just as today,
David of Sassoun and his Lightning-Sword!

"And at that time, only God will know
Who between us shall the sorrier be.
We who rise to wage a battle great,
Or you, who've made of us your enemy!"

1902

Translated by Aram Tolegian

QUATRAINS

1

O my native crickets dear
Now you chirrup, loud and clear. . . .
Invisible, sweet choristers,
Who is lending you an ear?

1916

2

My grief is a vast deep sea
Filled with gems that are fair to see.
My wrath is charged with love.
Full of stars is the night surrounding me.

1917

3

A thousand deaths dwell in my soul;
Death sits enthroned in my spirit's hall.
My heart is filled with the fear of death
For I am mortal just like all.

1917

4

Who knows the place where we've landed,
For how many days are we stranded?
When our hearts are empty, when love is gone,
'Tis in a fire we've landed.

1917

5

How many tortures have I stood,
What treachery have I withstood,
Borne with it all, forgiven and loved
And looked at evil as at good!

1917

6

Many a hand set fire to me
And made me burn like a storm-lit tree.
Become a flame, I issued light,
Now spent and dried myself I be.

1917

7

On all alike my spirit smiles
On good and evil, boons and guiles.
It shines all through my weary life,
On all my destined paths it shines.

1918

8

In my despair that knows no bounds,
Profound and low, a voice resounds
In my alert and wakeful ears—
The call of death, my steps it hounds.

1918

9

I shot and hurt a bird one day,
With bleeding wing it flew away.
Flying away I see it still,
With bleeding wing, to this very day.

1918

10

Two graves, one by the other's side,
Neighbors in eternal quiet;
Cold and sorrowful, they muse
On what from this world they took and hide.

1918

11

Under Autumn's gloomy look
A lark sits lost beside a brook
In the fields of my dear Lori,
Still gazing at the road I took.

1918

12

The bloody-mouthed cannibal, speaking with gestures
and leers,
Grew into a murderer after a million years.
Stoop-shouldered, with blood-smeared hands he keeps
groping on,
But still has a long way to go till Man he nears.

1918

13

A crystal night falls on the Eden of the East,
Where fairy palaces await my soul to feast.
What am I doing in this squalor, in this din?
Oh that I found a way to home, to peace!

1919

14

All around me men are dying or dead;
Life and death are confused in my head.
Existence or non-existence—
What matters when life has fled?

1919

15

O greedy, dissatisfied man, having long thoughts
   but short life,
Many like you passed away before your passions
   ran rife.
What did they take from life, that you could take
   with you too?
Seek Peace and try to enjoy your short days fraught
   with grief and strife.

1919

16

O mysterious Poet, unparalleled though unheard,
Your radiant looks spread songs that reach my heart
   without words.
Happy am I, your wonder-filled reader,
To read them, sweet as the songs of birds.

1919

17

Whether asleep or awake, my days passed by like
    dreams,
Day-dreams and dream-like days, short-lived
    as beacon-beams.
Dreams and longings all faded, none reached,
    none achieved,
Lost is my life like a bet, beaten like gamblers'
    schemes.
1919

18

Where can I expect more, in this or the other world?
Standing between the two, I muse—my view is blurred;
God himself, I think, is uncertain what to do,
To take me or leave me—who'll say the word?
1919

19

Generous, inexhaustible, giving like God, I grew tired;
Myself with a thirsting spirit, caring for men,
    I grew tired;
I long to meet someone to lavish love's riches on me;
Watching the way, awaiting, looking for me so tired.

1921

20

All my life I breathe the live breath of the living God
    everywhere,
Always I hear His voice, His incessant call
    everywhere.
My all-seeing, all-hearing soul is elevated and cleansed
By the melody and the murmur coming from
    everywhere.
1921

21

Overwhelmed by bloody disaster, strife and
    tumult of old,
The western slaves of machinery, filthy lucre
    and gold
Flee in awe from the waste of their long-dead souls
Here, to the East divine, the home that so dear
    I hold.
1921

22

As You take the blessings You gave me since
    life began,
I look to see how many are left till my race is run.
Amazed am I: You have given so freely, with
    generous hand;
How much must I yet return till I merge
    with You into one?
1921

23

High is the land of Armenia and Masis that touches
    the sky
Where my soul to converse with the Universe soars
    like a bird on high—
It started before the beginning of things,
    when existence was like non-existence,
To continue until the end of things, as long
    as time goes by.
1921

24

I turned my life into a square for all to tread
    who want;
How many flowers on that barren plot in my lifetime
    I could plant!
O God, Creator of this Earth and all the flowers it bears,
What answer will I give to You when You account
    demand?

1921

25

At my christening the heavens were church,
    a holy lamp the bright sun,
The rainbow held up its halo, my people's love
    was the font,
A mountain became my God-father, dew
    the life-giving myrrh,
And I was baptised by Him who created me as a bard.

1921

26

Brooklets murmur and run their course,
The thirsty yearn and pass away,
Poets, dreaming about life's source,
Utter their calls and go the same way.

1922

27

My soul is a thirsting traveler in the Universe divine,
Going its way through the world, indifferent to
    glory mundane.
Withdrawing from sinful Earth, soaring aloft
    to the skies,
To those remaining below my soul is already alien.

1922

So many pains and ruins of the past crowd in my heart,
Memories of past blessings are ousted from my heart.
At moments of melancholy I cannot recall
Was there ever a time when joy dwelt in my heart?

1922

Between two centuries rent,
Between two boulders pent,
I am lost between the old tsar
And a newly-found friend.

1917

I fool myself and flee in vain,
I am attached with bond and chain;
I suffer just like any other,
And share with them their common pain.

1917

My soul has come into its own,
Great as the Universe it has grown;
I am the lord of the whole world,
Yet who knows of it? I alone!

1917

32

Omar Khayam told his sweetheart: "Cautiously plant
   your foot;
Who knows on what beauty's eye your foot you may
   chance to put."
Friend, let us too walk gently, for we don't know
   whether we tread
Upon that beauty's eye or Khayam's unrivalled head.

1920

33

Your smile, like the sun at noon, shines hotly upon
   my face,
As mortally wounded I lie, awaiting death's last
   embrace,
Like a lightning-struck oak that stands drying day
   after day
Under the radiant sun's eternal life-giving rays.

1920

34

A thousand years before or since, what can ever
   matter—
I have existed and will exist, so what can ever matter!
I assume a thousand forms, all of them for a time,
With the soul universal my soul is one, so what
   can ever matter!

1921

35

All hearts are filled with the pain of our age,
The world's heart is filled with the pain of our age;
The whole ailing world pours into my heart
Torn open, filled with the pain of our age.

1921

36

Through time and distance you go, roads and ways,
No return do you ever know, roads and ways!
Who passed over you in their days,
And where did they go, roads and ways?

1922

SHORT STORIES

KIKOR

There was dissent in the household of Hambo, the peasant. He was for taking their twelve-year-old son Kikor to town to find him work so that he would get on in the world. But his wife would not agree.

"I don't want to throw my innocent child into that unjust world," she wept.

But Hambo would not heed her.

One calm, sad morning his family and the neighbors accompanied Kikor to the edge of the village, kissed him on both cheeks and saw him off on his journey.

His sister Zanny was crying, and little Gallo was baby-talking:

"Kikol, where you go, Kikol?"

Kikor kept looking back. He saw them still standing at the edge of the village, and his mother drying her eyes with her apron. He ran along beside his father, occasionally racing on ahead. Then one time when he looked around, the village was already hidden from view behind the hill.

From then on, Kikor kept lagging behind. "Come on now, Kikor my lad, come on, we're nearly there." Hambo kept calling to his son as he strode on, with a bag over his shoulder containing bread and cheese and a few plugs of tobacco.

In the evening, when the mountains were already behind them, the village came into sight once more in the distant haze.

"That's our house, isn't it Dad?" Kikor said pointing to the village, although their house was no longer visible.

They spent the first night in a village with an old friend of Hambo's.

The yellow samovar hissed away at one end of the divan. A young girl clinked the glasses as she washed them, and prepared the tea. She was wearing a pretty red dress. Kikor made a mental note that when he earned some money in the town, he would buy a dress like that for their Zanny.

After supper the host and Hambo leaned back and talked, puffing at their chibouks. They spoke about Kikor. The host praised Hombo for sparing no effort to have his son get on in the world. Then they went on to talk about the war, and the high food prices; but Kikor was so tired he fell asleep.

The following day they reached the town. There they put up with an old stable keeper and the next morning went down to the market.

"Hey, Uncle! Are you putting that boy into service?" a merchant inquired from inside a shop.

"I am, to be sure, good master!" replied Hambo, pushing Kikor towards him.

"Let me have him then. I'll take him on," proposed the merchant, who was called the bazaz Artem. So Hambo put Kikor into service at bazaz Artem's house. The terms were that Kikor would keep the house clean, wash the dishes, clean the shoes, take lunch to the shop, and carry out similar odd jobs for a year.

After a year bazaz Artem would take him to the shop as an apprentice and Kikor could thus gradually work his way up.

"I won't pay anything for five years," said bazaz Artem as they discussed the terms. "To tell you the truth, it's you who ought to be paying me to have your son trained. The boy knows nothing!"

"How could he know anything, kind master?" replied Hambo. "If he did, I wouldn't have brought him here. That's why I brought him—so's he'd learn something."

"He'll learn. He'll learn everything! And he'll learn it well! That fellow Nicol from your parts who has opened up his own shop learned all he knows from me. But in the end he stole a couple of spoons and one or two other things...."

"No, good master, this boy wouldn't steal. If he ever does such a thing, I'll come and throw him into the River Kura myself, I will."

"Well, if he's honest, we'll make a man of him!"

"That's what I want, kind master, to make a man of him. To have him learn languages, learn how to read and write, how to behave; to understand people, so that he won't be worthless like myself in this world! He's a bright lad. He's been to our village school and knows one letter from another. But, please, look after him well. He's a stranger here and young and innocent!"

Bazaz Artem reassured Hambo and went outside ordering in a loud voice:

"Bring tea and some food for these good people."

Father and son sat in bazaz Artem's kitchen.

"Now, it's up to you, Kikor lad. Let me see what sort of a boy you'll turn out to be! You must behave so that...so that....Well, I'll be damned if I know myself!" sighed Hambo and filled his chibouk.

Meanwhile Kikor stared around him curiously.

"Dad, haven't they got fireplaces here?"

"No, they use stoves. There, that's one over there!"

"Haven't they got any threshing-floors either?"

"These are townsfolk, my lad. They don't do threshing like us in the country!"

"Where do they get their bread from then?"

"They buy it for money. They buy bread, and butter, and milk, and yoghourt and wood, and even water for money!"

"Wow...!"

"Yes, this is Tiflis, lad, If you keep your wits about you, you'll learn a lot more!"

"Dad, have they got a church here?"

" 'Course they have. They're Christians like ourselves! Now, listen to me: don't you go stealing anything. They might leave some money about to try you out; don't you go near it. If you do pick it up, take it to the master or mistress and say: 'Whose money is this? Someone must have dropped it here on the floor.' If you don't...."

"Are there policemen here too, then?"

" 'Course there are! Now, don't you go wandering about here and there. And don't throw about any money that might come your way. There's a thousand and one things we need at home. Look after yourself well. Cover yourself up properly at night, so you won't catch cold! If you get the chance, send us a letter with anyone that comes here from our parts!"

As Hambo counselled his son between puffs at his chibouk, Kikor was dozing off.

"They'll give you scraps of dry bread and the leftovers from their meals to eat. There'll be times when they'll have their food and not give you any. But you mustn't take no notice: that's the lot of a servant.... But the days will go by and before you know it they'll pass...."

Hambo continued with his advice, but Kikor was already fast asleep, nestled up against his father. He had seen so much that was new to him during those two days that he was completely exhausted.

The shops full of fruit, all the different-colored

fabrics piled up like haystacks, all sorts of toys, the groups of children going to and from school, the carriages speeding along one after the other, the caravans of camels, the donkeys loaded with vegetables, the street-vendors with trays on their head—all the roar and bustle, the sounds of cries had mingled and were buzzing in his head. And weary from it all, he had fallen asleep leaning up against his father.

Meanwhile, bazaz Artem and his wife were arguing. She was complaining that the servant-boy was green and wild, straight down from the mountains, while her husband was delighted to have found an unpaid servant for a few years.

"He'll learn. He won't stay as he is!" he was saying to his wife.

"He'll learn, child, don't upset yourself so!" pleaded bazaz Artem's aged mother.

But Madame Natto would not be persuaded. She cried and cursed her luck.

Kikor was sitting alone in bazaz Artem's kitchen. He was already in service. He wore his master's old hat, which came down to his ears, his old shoes and a blue shirt. Thus transformed from head to foot, he was sitting and wondering why he had left his village for such a place, and what he should do now.

At that moment Madame Natto came in.

Kikor continued to sit where he was.

The mistress said something, but Kikor either did not hear or failed to understand.

"I'm talking to you, you little savage!"

Kikor was confused and broke out in a sweat. He wanted to ask her what she had said, but did not have the courage. The mistress went out angrily, saying: "To the devil with these savages who come here and become a menace! I tell him something and he neither moves nor utters a sound!"

"It's all over," Kikor thought. "But how quickly!..
And how badly it ended!...What am I to do now,
and with father gone...?"

He had considered the whole affair at an end, when
that kindly old woman, bazaz's mother, came in,
dressed in black and talking to herself.

"Why don't you stand up, my boy, when your
mistress comes in?" she advised Kikor. "When you
are asked a question, you should say something....
It really won't do."

The old lady was addressed by all as Mother.

Mother would teach Kikor what to do, how to light
the samovar, clean their shoes, wash the dishes, and
so on.

Everyone except old Mother was nasty to him. The
"apprentices" in the shop were always making fun of
him, pulling his nose, hitting him on the head and
ramming his hat down over his ears.

But he could bear all this. What he could not bear
was the hunger. At home, whenever he was hungry,
he used to go and help himself to some bread and
cheese, and eat it as he went off to play, or else put
it in his pocket and go to the fields, and then, when
he felt like it, sit down under a tree or beside a spring
and eat it.

It was different here. No matter how ravenous he
was he had to wait until mealtime; and even then the
others had to finish eating before he could begin. That
cursed hour would be so long coming that the poor
boy would be in agony, his heart in his mouth.

Having been patient once, twice, ten times, he began
to cast his eyes around the kitchen to see if there was
some morsel or other to eat, in order to allay his
hunger until it was time for the meal.

At first, he would put in his mouth whatever he

could find: a dry crust of bread, a nibbled bone, or any other leftovers. But after a while he thought of looking in the kitchen cupboards. Then he took to pulling out pieces of half-cooked meat from the saucepan!

But supposing they caught him red-handed?

How terrible that would be!

What would he do then?

And Kikor began to think of running away.

But where could he go all alone? Not knowing the way, not knowing anybody.

Besides, his father had worried so much, had talked to him and advised him: "The days will go by, son, and before you know it they'll pass...."

And his father's hoarse voice now sounded inside Kikor's head: "The days kill go by...they'll pass... they'll pass...!

The bell rang.

Kikor sprang to his feet. He had been told that whenever the doorbell rang, he was to see who it was and what they wanted. He went out onto the balcony and looking down saw a gentleman and several ladies standing at the door.

"Here, who are you, eh?" he called down.

They looked up. The ladies laughed, while the gentleman adjusted his spectacles and asked:

"Is your mistress at home?"

"What's your business?" asked Kikor.

The laughter below increased.

"You're being asked whether she is at home or not!" the gentleman snapped.

"What would you be wanting her for?"

Hearing the raised voices, Madame Natto came out.

"You little stinker! Go and open the door—on the double!" she screamed, and began cursing both Kikor and her husband. But soon the guests appeared and she advanced to greet them with a smile:

"Oh, hello, hello! What a nice surprise that you should drop in like this!"

"Where did you dig him up?" asked the gentleman, sizing up Kikor from head to foot.

"What, have you taken a fancy to him? You can have him if you like!" said the hostess jokingly, and the visitors went inside laughing.

Madame Natto hurriedly sent Kikor off on an errand and she immediately followed the others inside.

After the inquiries as to one another's health, the guests related the whole story of their arrival.

"Oh, he'll be the death of me!" complained Madame Natto. "If only you knew how I have to suffer through him! I keep saying that we should turn him out into the street, but you know what Artem is like. He says, 'It's a shame, he's only a peasant boy. Let him stay; he'll hardly eat us out of house and home. He'll learn!' But when? He's quite worn me out!"

"Oh, don't talk about the servant problem, It's quite impossible!" all the other ladies chimed in.

Then they chatted away for about half an hour, about this and that, about servants, and about news in the town. They were still in the middle of their conversation when Kikor came in, hot and sweaty.

"I have brought the fruit, madame!"

"Very well, that will be all!" said the mistress blushing, and the guests laughed.

"Madame, the master said that cherries were dear and there was no need to get any!"

This caused some of the guests to burst into gales of laughter, which they tried to suppress with their handkerchiefs; while others, in order to cover up the hostess's confusion, confirmed that cherries were indeed very expensive and that no one would dream of buying them at that time of year. Besides, they protested, there was no need for her to go to any such bother.

The hostess, blushing to the roots of her hair, tried to put matters right somehow.

"Goodness knows what my husband said. I'm sure this idiot misunderstood him!"

"May God strike me down if I tell a lie!" swore Kikor, thus clinching the matter.

After seeing the guests off, Madame Natto talked loudly and angrily to herself as she cleared the fruit from the table. She swore at Kikor, enumerating his misdeeds one by one, and cursing her luck and her husband.

"My dear child, he's green. He'll learn! Why do you upset yourself so? Oh, God, when will Thou come and take my soul unto Thee...?" sighed old Mother.

"I've had enough! If he's green, you can go and sort him out between you! I'm not your slave, you know!" replied the daughter-in-law, raising her voice even more, and she continued grumbling and cursing until her husband came home.

As soon as she heard her husband's footsteps, she began to cry and to shout louder, knocking about the pots and pans.

"Throw him out, I say! I'll do the servant's work myself! That's what comes of saving! If you pay wages, you get a proper servant! I'd rather do a servant's work as well than get upset like this every day!"

"What's happened?" asked bazaz Artem, stopping in the middle of the room.

"I'll tell you what's happened: you've made me look like a fool in front of people! That's what happened!" his wife flew at him and told him about the incident with the cherries.

"What!" exclaimed bazaz Artem. "Why, the...!"

"Oh, Lord!" sighed the kind old woman, shuffling

about helplessly.

Artem called Kikor and he entered the room, with his heart pounding.

"Come closer!" Artem shouted.

Kikor was terrified by the man's fearsome expression and stood rooted to the spot.

"I told you to come closer!"

This time Kikor made to move, but still remained where he was.

"You stupid oaf! I told you to go and tell your mistress that the cherries were dear. Not to blurt it out in front of the guests!"

"I...I...told the mistress..." Kikor stammered, but the words were not yet out of his mouth when a blow struck him on the face. He saw stars, his head struck the wall and he fell to the floor. Bazaz Artem started kicking him, all the time repeating: "Cherries are dear, are they...? Cherries are dear, are they?"

Old Mother, shaking all over, intervened and tried to pull away her enraged son. She was joined in her efforts by his wife, and the children began to scream; whereupon bazaz Artem stepped back panting and still repeating: "So cherries are dear, are they...?" and glaring furiously at Kikor, who was huddled up in the corner, trembling like a leaf and groaning piteously:

"Oh, mother, mother...oh, mother...."

Seeing that Kikor was hopeless as a servant in the house, they took him to the shop. There he had to deliver goods to customers, fold up rolls of fabrics, keep the shop clean and, when he had nothing else to do, attract customers.

One day Kikor was taking lunch to the shop. Looking run down and pallid, and dragging along in boots that were far too big for him, he made his way across the bridge with the dinner-can. He stopped and looked

112

down: the River Kura reared up and struck against the high wall of the caravanserai, foaming, swirling and eddying, then raced away subdued and swished on under the bridge.

A green boat was floating about near the bank. There were two men in it, one of them casting a net, the other steering the boat.

"Now he'll bring it in!" Kikor said to himself and stood there watching the fishermen. The net came out of the water empty.

"Now this one is for my luck," said Kikor as the net was cast again. His luck also turned out to be empty.

"This one is for our Zanny's luck."

But this time too it came out empty.

"And this one for Gallo's luck." Gallo was also unlucky.

"And this one. . . ."

But at that moment, a clamor arose at the gates of the caravanserai. A Persian was making a monkey perform as he chanted:

"Hey now, monkey, come on.

Freeze your neck like a post!

Now hump your back like an old man!

Now dance away like a youth!"

A dense crowd had gathered around the Persian and others were running up from all sides. Kikor ran up too. He tried to squeeze between the people and get to the front, but he could not. He craned his neck, stood up on tiptoe and strained to see what was happening in the middle.

"What're you pushing like that for, you little brat! Go wherever you were sent!" barked some young fellow and struck him on the head.

Kikor suddenly came to his senses and rushed off to the shop.

That evening Kikor sat huddled in the kitchen. The tears had not yet dried on his face, his cheeks still stung from the master's blows, and the mistress's shouts had only just died down, when Vasso, one of the shop assistants, came in whistling. Noticing Kikor, he stopped immediately and, assuming a serious expression on his otherwise roguish face, asked, threateningly:

"Did you delay at the club, you little savage? Or did you have important business to attend to with the governor of the province, eh?"

Kikor did not even raise his head.

"Well, come on, let's hear what you've got to say for yourself?"

Kikor remained silent.

"Do you hear me? Where were you today, eh? Did you want me to starve to death or something?"

As he spoke he gradually approached Kikor, then stopped and suddenly struck him on the head. The little boy protected his head with his two hands and pressed himself against the wall. Vasso was about to hit him again, but bazaz Artem's voice was heard from outside. He had returned home.

"You'll see what he's got in for you now!" threatened Vasso.

"They'll kill me now," thought Kikor and his poor little heart sank with terror.

Bazaz Artem had already given him a sound beating in the shop and now only ordered that he should be given no food so that he should know the meaning of hunger.

The danger had passed.

Kikor calmed down, although he could hear the mistress's voice screaming:

"But why do you still keep him? Throw him out and let him get lost! Throw him out...."

Kikor curled up, pulled the blanket over his head and hid there.

"O moonlit night, I have no sleep.

He who sees me thinks I have no home, alas, no home...." Vasso sang as he ate his supper. From time to time, Kikor peered out cautiously from under his blanket, stole a glance at him and again closed his eyes. He had not had a bite to eat that day, he had been beaten and had cried his heart out, and now he was lying there hungry and unable to sleep.

"Well? What's the matter? Can't you sleep without something inside you, eh?" remarked the mischievous Vasso and gave Kikor a piece of bread and some cheese. "There, take it and eat it under your bed-clothes. Only don't let the master see you!"

Kikor snatched the bread and cheese, thrust his head back under the bedclothes, and as he chewed his mind went back to his home, to the days when he used to play freely in the fields, and eat to his heart's content; to those evenings when his parents used to quarrel about taking him to town... his mother would cry, not wanting to let him to go....

"Oh, dear mother, how well your heart knew what would happen!" sighed Kikor as he munched the bread and cheese under the bedclothes, his ears pricked in case the master came in.

And in the morning he was back at the shop again.

Kikor stood at the shop-door calling out for customers and loudly praising the quality of their goods.

"Why're you standing there mum? Call out, boy, call out! Your mouth isn't full of water, it it?"

"Come along, this way now! This way...!" Kikor called out.

Inside the shop, they split their sides with laughter. The shop assistants told him he should drag customers into the shop, and taking their words in all seriousness he would often seize some passer-by by the clothes, drag him roughly and persistently towards the shop and not release him until the man lost his patience. Then Kikor would go back to his place and call out again.

On hot summer days, after standing at the door for a long time, he would sometimes fall asleep sitting on one of the piles of material in front of the shop.

Then, either his mischievous friends or the neighbors would hold some snuff under his nose, and he would fly to his feet sneezing.

The tradesmen, limp from the heat, would be greatly amused, while bazaz Artem, after laughing heartily, would shout at him:

"Asleep, eh, you little savage? Call out!"

"Come along, this way now! This way...!" Kikor would cry out.

One day, as Kikor was calling out for customers, two peasants came out of a shop opposite. He ran across to them and threw his arms around them.

"Hey, boy, I would never have recognized you! Well, well, well!" one of the peasants exclaimed with astonishment and turned to his companion:

"Know who he is Bagho?"

"I would have known him by his eyes!" boasted the other.

Kikor had indeed changed greatly. He had grown very thin, and his clothes were different too. He had changed practically beyond recognition.

"Hey, boy, he's turned into a real city slicker! ...Just look at his clothes and what a fine young lad he's become!" said the two peasants with admiration.

"Well, well! See what Hambo's done for his son! And our boys back in the village are tending swine!"

Meanwhile Kikor was bombarding them with questions.

"How's my mother? How are the children? Why didn't father come? Has our cow calved yet? Has anyone died in the village?"

"They are all well and ·send you their love," replied the peasants. "Ghoukas Souknants died and the old woman Bodjourants, but the rest are well."

"But why didn't my father come?"

"He wanted to, but how could he? He's the only man in the house and he's got all the work to do!"

"Didn't they send me anything?"

"They've got nothing to send you; you know what your home's like, don't you? And food has been short this year. Your father has only just managed to make ends meet. What do you expect from them? Now, if you have anything, you send it to them. They need money; they haven't got a kopek between them."

"Have any of the family been ill?"

"No! But the Mirzans' shed collapsed on top of your cow, Dzaghik, and she died."

"Dzaghik died...?"

"Your poor mother cried so much her eyes were swollen."

So anything, one of the peasants brought out a letter and gave it to Kikor, adding:

"Anything else? We're going back now and we won't be seeing you again. If you've got anything to send your mother or your sister, we'll take it back with us."

"How can I send them anything, I don't get any money yet! Only...!"

"Only what?"

"Only... I want to go back with you. I miss our village and the family, and...."

"Now, now! And we thought you had become a man and learned something! What sort of talk is that? You're living like a master here, your clothes are new, your hands and feet are clean! If you can find a place for our boys, we'll bring them to town too! They say, 'A swine's head was put on a rug and it rolled back and fell in the mind,' that's just about you!"

The peasants admonished him thus, wished him well and departed.

When they had left, Kikor retired to his corner and opened his father's letter.

"The city of Tiflis,

"My dear son, Kikor,

"We are alive and well and wish you good health too, amen. Much love from Dad, Mom, Zanny, Mossy, Mikich and Gallo, amen. Our dear son, Kikor, I must tell you that things are very hard with us and they are pressing us for taxes and we have no money; your Mam and Zanny have practically nothing to wear, and we are really in bad shape. Kikor, love, send us a few rubles and a letter about yourself! Dzaghik has died and your Mam and Zanny are almost naked."

Kikor read the letter and pondered as he stood there, worrying about home. The words in the letter seared his heart: "your Mom and Zanny are almost naked....We are really in bad shape...."

"Call out, boy! What have you been doing out there? Have you fallen asleep?" they shouted from inside.

"Come along, this way now! This way...!" cried out Kikor, standing at the shop-door.

Winter came. An icy snow-storm blew noisily over the town. It whistled and howled through the streets. It darted into corners, looking for the poor and the unclothed, seeking forlorn children away from their homes.

And it found Kikor.

He was wearing a thin blouse, as he stood at the shop door, calling out:

"Come along, this way now! This way...!"

The malicious cold came and whistled through his bones like an invisible sword. Kikor shuddered.

Emaciated and enfeebled as he was, it was enough. He took to his bed.

Kikor lay ill in bazaz Artem's kitchen. Old Mother would go in several times a day, muttering to herself.

"What would you like, Kikor, my son?" she would ask.

"Water...!"

Mother would give him some. The sick boy would take hold of the tumbler with trembling hands, gulp it down greedily and ask for more.

"This doesn't cool my heart, Mother...! I want some cold water from our springs, Mother...! I'm going home...I want my mother...."

Bazaz Artem was worried. He looked about and found someone from Hambo's parts, and sent word for him to come. Meanwhile he took Kikor to the city hospital.

There were many patients there, lying in rows. They groaned dolefully and stared up at the ceiling with their glassy eyes.

Kikor was laid among them.

There his father found him.

"What's the matter, Kikor, my boy?" Hambo inquired painfully.

In his fever Kikor was unaware of his father's presence.

"Kikor, my dear, I'm here..! It's your father...!"

The sick boy did not hear him. He was raving, "Mikich, Zanny, Dad, Mom...!"

"I'm here, Kikor love. Your Mom's sent me to take you back home.... Won't you come? Mikich and Zanny are standing on the roof right now, watching the road for you. What do you say to that? Say something, Kikor love...!"

"This way! This way...!" cried the sick boy, uttering disjointed words and laughing in his delirium.

Two days later, Hambo was on his way back to the village.

He had buried Kikor and was returning home. Under his arm, he carried his clothes, so that his mother could cry over them. In one of his pockets they had found a handful of shiny buttons, bits of colored paper, pieces of material and a few safety-pins. He had evidently collected and kept these for his sister Zanny....

Hambo walked on deep in thought. It was not so long since he had gone to the town with Kikor along that same road. Here was the place he had said, "Dad, my feet are sore."

And there was the tree under which they had stopped for a rest....

There was the place he had said, "Dad, I'm thirsty...."

And there was the fountain from which they had drunk.

Everything was there, everything except him.

The following day, as Hambo was crossing the mountains, the village appeared in the distance.

Outside the village Mom, Zanny, Mikich, and Mossy stood waiting, and little Gallo called from his mother's arms:

"Come on, Kikol, come on...!"

MY FRIEND NESO

I

We were a group of village children—all friends.

There was no school, no lessons, no education. Left as we were entirely to our own devices we did nothing but play together all the time. How we played! And how fond of one another we were and how used to one another! Whenever we were hungry, we would run home, snatch a piece of bread from the basket and a piece of cheese from the cask and hurry back to find one another. In the evenings we used to gather together to romp about and laugh or tell stories.

One of the group was called Neso. He knew so many, many stories that there was just no end to them.

On moonlit summer nights we used to sit about on logs at our door and stare in bright-eyed admiration at Neso's face glowing with enthusiasm. He would tell us of the Houri Fairies, of the Emerald Bird, the world of Light and Darkness....

"Neso, Neso! Now tell us about the Blind King... the story of the Tout Bird, the story of the Bald Man and the Kasak."

II

It so happened that a school was opened in our village. Some thirty children including myself were sent to it. But since the yearly fee for each child was three rubles, most of the village children were unable to attend because their parents could not afford it. Thus, most of my playmates were left out, and among them Neso.

This was the first time that we had been separated from one another, and we were separated by the school and the teacher. For the first time we became conscious of the fact that there were those of us who had and others who had not. Even today Neso's bitter crying still rings in my ears. He was rolling on the ground before their house yelling that he also wanted to go to school. And his father's voice too still rings in my ears, "I haven't got the wherewithal! I just haven't got it! How can I pay what I haven't got? If I had three rubles I'd buy bread to feed you. But I haven't and there you are, hungry!"

Neso and the other of our playmates who were unable to go to school used to come and gather in the doorway, listening to what we were doing. But the teacher would not let them in, and would drive them away. He would not even allow them to play with us during the breaks, saying that outside children had no business playing with the school-children. They would squat about at the foot of the school walls waiting for our lessons to be over so that we could all go home together.

During my first year at school I gradually made friends with new boys. By the end of the school year Neso and my other friends outside the school no longer came to squat near the walls to wait for me.

III

After a couple of years at our village school, my father sent me to the school in the nearby town. This was an entirely new world. The houses were white with red roofs and the people well-dressed and clean. The school itself was large and beautiful, and there was not only one teacher, as in our village, but a number of them, and there were even lady-teachers, which was a novelty and surprise for me, but a very agreeable one.

My clothes were also changed to suit the place and the school.

I wore a town pupil's uniform, smart and clean. And thus transformed, I returned to the village for the holidays.

Hearing of my arrival, Neso and my other friends had come early in the morning and were milling about outside our house and murmuring at the foot of the wall. I came out and approached them. I do not remember how we greeted one another. All I recollect is that gone was the former frankness and intimacy. They first turned their attention to my clothes. Neso even went so far as to joke about my short school tunic, "Just like a bobtail magpie...." All of them laughed and I was very hurt but said nothing. Then Neso stroked my clothes, the others followed suit and they expressed surprise at the softness of the material. That day, for the first time, I took a close look at their clothes and noticed how dirty and ragged they were. And indeed our entire village looked dirty and poverty-stricken.

IV

After a couple of years at this second school, my father sent me to the city, to a still bigger school. When I returned home, my former playmates, who were already strapping youths, came to greet me like the rest of the villagers, and stood with them at a respectful distance. Only once, in the course of the conversation in which others put questions to me, Neso asked, "Remember how we used to sit about on logs at your door and tell stories?"

"Do I remember!?" I exclaimed. "How could I forget? It's one of my very best childhood memories."

Neso seemed delighted, but he still remained aloof, and like a stranger.

When the time came for me to go back to school, it so happened that we hired the horse of Neso's father for me to ride on. Neso was to walk behind the horse. As we started, I on horseback and Neso in rags and worn-out sandals walking alongside, I found this weighed too heavily on my heart. After a while I declared that I preferred to walk and dismounted. So we went on either walking together or else taking turns riding. Neso was very pleased at this, but I noticed that he ascribed my act not to my kindness and friendly feeling but to my foolishness. I was greatly upset by this, but a bigger disappointment awaited me.

On our way we stopped to rest and have a bite. When we got to the watermelon, I produced my pocket knife and handed it over to Neso to cut it. As we were preparing to leave I noticed that the knife had disappeared. Neso insisted that he had returned it to me and that I had put it away in my pocket. Although I knew very well that he had not returned it to me, I searched my pockets just the same and we set off again. There was no doubt in my mind but that he had stolen my knife, and later people in the village reported having seen him with it. I travelled on with a heavy heart; not because I had lost my knife, but because I had lost something else, far more valuable, a very precious thing which was incomprehensible to Neso. . . . When we reached our destination and it was time for Neso to go back, I presented him a cape on top of the charge for the horse. Yet his only reaction was to ask me rudely, "What about a tip then?"

Extremely abashed, I gave him a tip too. But since then every time I remember my childhood days and those nights with our group sitting on logs under the moon and Neso telling stories, my heart fills with grief and sorrow.

V

"Neso is poor. Neso is ignorant. Neso is crushed by the hardships of the peasant's bitter lot. If he too had received an education, and had security, he might have become a good man, perhaps far better than I...." I always think thus now whenever I remember Neso, and I try to justify him, understand him, and love him again as I loved him in childhood. I always want to have in my mind's eye the picture of Neso of the quiet, starry, moonlit nights. But in vain, all in vain; for at once another picture comes forth, a shameful and painful one.

When I had graduated and was making my way in life, I returned once more to our village. Going to the plaza I found a noisy crowd of villagers gathered there and in their midst Neso with drooping head, his hands tied with a rope.

To my inquiries as to what was the matter, they answered that he had been thieving. I intervened and got them to release him. But in my mind's eye I still see him, his head hung low and his hands tied with a rope, standing in the blazing sun, and the crowd roaring around him.

Thieving, tying people's hands with a rope, and beatings are quite usual occurrences in our village. Yet this scene sticks firmly in my mind, as does that other picture: Neso the small boy, Neso the story-teller, seated on a log on moonlit nights, the innocent and naive Neso, my childhood friend Neso.

THE CONSTRUCTION OF
THE RAILWAY

One evening in 1898, shortly before the opening of the railway from Tiflis to Kars, we were sitting about on logs before the house of Master Ohannes in a village in the Lori district, having a chat. Master Ohannes was telling us how the construction of the railway had begun.

"One day our Simon and I were out cutting wood in the lower valley by the river," he began. "Suddenly we saw several men wearing white caps making their way up the bank."

"Well, well, Simon," says I.

"What is it?"

"Something's afoot," I says.

"Why so? They're just strangers going their way. Perhaps they're lost."

"No," said I. "Something's afoot. You mark my words."

"When we got back to the village we noticed a white pole on the roof of Tersan's flourmill."

"Well, well, Simon!" says I.

"What is it?"

"Now do you see?" I says.

"See what?"

"You wait." I says. "You'll see."

Not long after that we saw it announced in the newspaper that the railway was coming our way. . . .

"Well, well, Simon!" says I.

"What is it?"

"Now do you see?" I says. "I was right, wasn't I?"

"So you were, confound it!" cried the hunter Osep, interrupting Master Ohannes's story.

"Why, now, what harm is there in a railway?" put in some of the villagers.

"Harm, and nothing else! Why, it came hooting into the valleys and frightened away the deer. It's as if they didn't exist," complained Osep.

"It's more than the deer, begad," said a shepherd, leaning on his stick. "When I look down into the valley from the mountainside and see them blasting the rocks, my heart bleeds as if my own child was being disembowelled by the enemy and I was standing by helpless...."

"There'll be plenty of destruction alright!" some sighed in agreement.

And an argument flared up about the benefit and the harm of the railway.

During the argument one of the workers on the railway came up from the valley and approached us.

"Good evening," he said.

"Good evening, Master!"

"I need some flour. Will anyone sell me some?" the stranger asked, addressing us all.

"Where are you from?" asked Master Ohannes.

"I am from the land of the Ottomans."

"Master Ohannes, ask him what town he's from," said a curious villager.

"What town are you from, my friend?" Master Ohannes asked again.

"From Sivaz."

"From Sivaz!" Master Ohannes repeated wisely, lingering over the last syllable.

"What did he say, Master Ohannes?"

"Sivaz...."

"May your house stand firm in Sivaz!" cried some of the villagers clapping their hands and laughing.

"How many months' journey is it from there to here?" Master Ohanes continued his questioning.

"Three months."

"Phew!" they all exclaimed in amazement.

"Welcome, stranger! Sit down and do us the honor of eating with us!"

"Thank you, kindly, but I'm in a hurry. If someone'll sell me some flour I'll be going."

"Hey there! Bring out a pot of flour," Master Ohannes called out from the door. "And fill it full!"

One of the women brought out a pot of flour and went to pour it into the stranger's bag, but he would not let her.

"How much do I owe you?" he asked.

"Come. Pour it into your bag first!" urged Master Ohannes.

"No. First tell me the price."

"Go on pour it in, and then we'll tell you. If it's too dear, you can always pour some back."

The stranger opened his bag, and the woman poured the flour in and returned to the house.

"Right.... Now, how much do I owe you?" asked the stranger pulling out his purse from under his belt.

"Nothing, stranger. You owe us nothing. It's all yours for free. In our land we are not in the habit of charging strangers for food. We have no such custom...." said Master Ohannes, puffing at his pipe.

The stranger was somewhat embarrassed, protested weakly and left.

There followed a short silence, then someone said:

"A few days ago one of them came for yoghurt. The women offered him some. When he'd eaten it, he stood up and wanted to know the price. 'The price of what?' I ask him. 'Of the yoghurt,' he says. 'My good man, enough of that,' I says. 'Stop such talk or the sheep's milk may dry up.'"

"Well, lads, what is to be done about it then? Are we to let them come and eat and take food away with them as long as they like? How many of them have been coming these last few days? Not so long ago I myself poured out a potful of flour for one of them. How long can this go on?" put in the younger brother of Master Ohannes.

"If he comes again, give him another pot. . . ." said Master Ohannes quietly raising his head.

"May there always be plenty in your home!" exclaimed some of the old men.

"Whoever comes, by thunder, from Sivaz or where have you, should we serve them with food free of charge, as if we work for them! I say welcome! Welcome to all! But if you want food, pay for it then take it!" said the younger brother.

And they began to argue. Master Ohannes got all worked up and the din increased.

"Toot, toot. . ." whistled the train down below.

The railway had just entered our valleys.

1898

THE BET

1

Where the mountains meet they form a large gorge named Moot Dzor.

Moot Dzor separates the Armenians from the Turks. On one side the Turkish nomads pitch their tents on the slopes, on the other the Armenians.

But their bold young men steal across the deep gorge in the darkness of night and lift one another's sheep, and drive away horses, cows and oxen. Overtaking the thieves in the pastures, the shepherds fall on them with staves.

From time to time one hears a shrill drawn-out call spreading from one of the mountain sides. "He-e-e-lp!" And that ominous cry echoes over the mountains and immediately both sides are up in arms.

2

A Turk, Hapic-oglu by name, had put up his tent and made camp on one side of Moot Dzor. He gazed arrogantly and threateningly at the Armenians opposite. His men were the most notorious thieves in those mountains. Outlaws took refuge in his place and gangs of bandits passing through the mountains found hospitality under his roof.

One evening, he was reclining in his tent, talking with his usual guests—well-known robbers passing through the mountains.

"Strange that your lads should leave those Armenians there in peace," ventured one of the guests, a Kurd.

"They're none too easy to deal with," replied the host.

"What, them!?"

"That's right, them. There is a shepherd among them called Chati. I'll call brave the man who challenges him single-handed," said Hapic-oglu.

"Pooh!" the bandit exclaimed scornfully and jerked upright touched to the quick. "What will you give me if I see to it that he does not see the light of another day and no smoke rises on yonder side in the morning?"

"The blue horse goes as the reward!"

"Your hand on it."

They shook hands and the bet was concluded.

4

The nights in Moot Dzor arē terribly dark. That night was pitch black and a steady rain was falling. The Armenian camp was asleep. Now and then the shepherds' faint calls were heard from here and there, indicating that they were alert.

In the middle of the night there came a pounding of hoofs past the tents. The dogs barked and started in pursuit, the sheep bolted, the horses ran away, and the cattle dispersed. The shepherds shouted for help, guns spat fire, and all these terrors and shrieks mixing with the darkness, the torrential downpour and the thunder, made it a truly infernal night.

"They've drawn away the dogs. Protect the camp!" roared Chati, the giant shepherd.

The cry "They've drawn away the dogs!" was taken up and echoed on all sides and terror seized the camp. For in the mountains everybody knows only too well what "They've drawn away the dogs" means.

It is customary for one or two bandits to first break into a camp and scare the sheep, horses and cattle and create panic. The dogs give chase, and are thus led far away from the camp. Then, with the camp in turmoil and the dogs gone, their accomplices attack and take advantage of the confusion and the darkness to make off with the animals.

The second attack was not long in coming, and a great commotion ensued. Fire-arms went into action, everything got confused in the darkness, and pandemonium broke loose in the valley.

Nothing was visible in the pitch darkness. The lightning flashes would illuminate the terrible scene for an instant, but the human eye could not discern anything in the chaos. Eyes could not see, but the reports of gunfire and the shepherds' cries indicated the direction of the chase.

By and by those sounds also receded, dwindled and died away.

The rain continued steadily and the clouds cracked and rumbled over the distant mountains.

5

At daybreak the lads returned From the distance their cheerful talk and peals of laughter could be heard through thick mist. They brought the cattle back safe and sound and then gathered together in the tent of Chati the shepherd to have breakfast.

They had brought with them a Kurdish tunic, shield

and sword.

Soon the news spread that the boys had killed a Kurd, and curious mountaineers crowded in and about the tent.

Chati's mother was cooking a meal on the fire for the hungrey shepherds and droning to herself:

"My son, the fellow may have a mother, too. . .

My son, his mother may be expecting him now. . .

My son, she will say her son has not returned. . .

My son, she will wait and he'll not come. . ."

Other women joined her, shaking their heads. Meanwhile the shepherds were recounting what had happened.

"We grouped together from all sides and drove them down into the hollow. As we cornered them there, they left the livestock and took to their heels to a man. I pursued one and drove him up against a steep rock. Seeing there was no escape, he turned round, drew his sword and charged me crying: 'Away! or I'll cut you in two.' Cut me in two, will you!? I whirled my cudgel, and struck him such a whacking blow on the shoulder!"

"Bravo!" cried the listeners.

"And he crashed to the ground," said Chati bringing his story to an end.

There was a peal of delighted laughter from the mountaineers.

6

A few weeks had passed since the event when one day the dogs barked violently. People came out and found an old Kurd calling from below the camp.

"What do you want, good man?"

"I want the tent of the shepherd Chati," said the Kurd.

He was brought to the tent. Chati put food before

133

the guest. They made small talk until the old man had eaten his fill. When the Kurd had done, Chati asked:

"I hope all is well. What brings you here, good man?"

"Some weeks ago a young Kurd was killed here," said the old man.

"That's right," replied the shepherd.

"They say you killed him."

"That's right, I did."

"I am his father," said the old man. "I have come to tell you that you acted justly and fairly. You did not kill him on the road from an ambush. You did not kill him in the midst of flock. You did not kill him in his own home.... How many times did I tell him, 'My son, lay off, stop all this mischief, give up those mates of yours. People have not toiled for you to loot....' He did not listen to me. Evidently, such was his fate," said the Kurd and then lowered his head and fell silent.

"May you remain firm in your faith, for you speak fair," the mountaineers voiced from all sides and then were quiet.

"You have acted fairly," went on the old man raising a thick voice from the bottom of his heart. "Only his mother....Well, she is his mother after all.... She is eating her heart out....Give me his clothes. Let me take them to her to shed her tears on, quench her longing and put her heart at peace."

Chati produced the blood-stained tunic, shield and sword and handed them over to the old man. Then he presented him with a sheep, accompanied him past the dogs, and saw him off.

"Well, good-bye, my boy," said the old Kurd and left.

"Fare thee well, good man!"

1908

UNCLE KHECHAN

"Good morning!"

"Welcome, welcome, Uncle Khechan. Hey there, wife, bring some tea! Bring food and drink for Uncle Khechan! Well, I hope nothing is wrong, Uncle Khechan. What brings you to town?"

"What could be wrong? I just missed you, that's all. I said to myself 'Life has its up and downs. We're here today and gone tomorrow. I'll go down and see how they're keeping.' "

"Thank you, thank you, Uncle Khechan."

Uncle Khechan talked about this and that, drank tea, ate, then fell silent and puffed away at his chibouk.

After a while he removed the chibouk from his mouth and said, "A fine business! What are we going to do?"

"What are you talking about, Uncle Khechan?"

"Our boy is being called into the army."

"Really? But what can I do?"

"What do you mean, 'What can I do?' When your aunt's eyes are red with weeping for the boy!"

"Well, tell me what I can do. I am ready to do whatever I can."

"First let's get his birth certificate and then see what we can do about it."

"All right, come on!"

We went to the church council. I asked the registrar and he produced the registers of the year indicated by

Uncle Khechan. We looked for his son here, there and everywhere, but he was nowhere to be found.

"Brother, how is it possible?"

"There's just no record, Uncle Khechan."

"Look further down, some years later. We may have made a mistake."

The registrar produced other books. We searched but could find no record of the lad.

"We must have made a mistake. . . . Certainly, we've made a mistake," said Uncle Khechan again. According to my reckonings the boy must be older. How silly of me! I should have said further up, not further down."

"All right, Uncle Khechan, we'll look some years earlier too."

More registers were brought, and we went on searching.

He was not to be found there either.

"He's not there. The priest didn't register him."

"Well, what's to be done?"

If he's not registered, there's nothing we can do about it. Let's go home, Uncle Khechan."

"What do you mean, 'Go home'? Your aunt is weeping her heart out.

"Well, what can we do if he isn't registered?"

We went out. We had hardly gone some fifty paces when Uncle Khechan stopped.

"Just a minute!"

"What is it, Uncle Khechan?"

"What have we achieved and where are we going?"

"What do you mean, 'Where are we going'? Home, of course."

"A fine business!"

"Well, what can we do?"

"I told them at home I could depend on you and came straight here. Now what shall I tell them when

136

I get back?"

"Well, what do you thing I can do, Uncle Khechan? The registers are there, we went through so many years, up and down the records, here, and everywhere there. He's just not there!"

"What do you mean, 'Not there'? How is it that everybody's child is there all right and just mine happens not to be there?"

"Well, that's the way it is. What can we do about it?"

Uncle Khechan did not utter another word all the way home. When we arrived my wife asked, "Well, what have you achieved?"

"We shall see," answered Uncle Khechan.

"What shall we see? There's no record in the register, and that's all there is to it," I put in.

Uncle Khechan sighed. "That's all there is to it, is it? And I'm to retrace my steps back home, I suppose," he concluded and sat there with a grieved air, sucking extra hard at his chibouk.

Dinner time came, and we ate in silent. Suddenly Uncle Khechan stopped eating and addressed me: "And when I get home, what shall I tell your aunt?"

"About what?"

"The birth certificates."

"Ye Gods! He's not registered! He's not in the books! The priest didn't register him. He's not there!"

"What do you mean, 'Not there'?"

Uncle Khechan sighed again and took up the chibouk. After dinner I stole into my room to have a rest. I was thinking what funny people our peasants were. . . . Just then Uncle Khechan came in, "Taking a nap?"

"Yes."

"Is this a time for sleeping?"

"But what can I do, Uncle Khechan?"

"I have come here in need for help and you're doing nothing to help."

"What am I supposed to do?"

"What do you suggest we do about the certificate?"

"You're an extraordinary man. I'm telling you in your own tongue, man, that the name's not there! It's not there, Uncle Khechan!"

"All right, all right, but why do you get so worked up? So it's not there, then I'm going home. Goodbye," he said and went out muttering.

"Good-bye. But what can I do if he's not there?"

When I woke up and came out of my room I saw Uncle Khechan sitting on the balcony sucking at his chibouk. I took my hat and was about to leave.

"Where are you going?" Uncle Khechan called after me.

"What do you suggest?"

"Nothing."

"Are you going out?"

"Yes, I am."

"Won't you call again at the church council?"

"No, I can't."

After this event Uncle Khechan returned to his village and told his neighbors that he had been in difficulty, had come to town and asked me to help him, and I had refused. Nobody had paid any attention to him and he had been completely ignored.

1910

THE DEER

Once, on a September night, Osep, the hunter from our village, took me to the narrow Yeghud defile to hunt deer. The deer used to come down through the defile into the valleys below to graze at night, drink water before the dawn and then return to their rocky "homes."

We were to spend the night at the cabin of Ovakim the gardener, so that we would not have far to go to the hunting ground at daybreak to watch for the game.

There were three of us: the hunter Osep, a boy from our village carrying Osep's equipment and myself.

We walked on with the cruel joy with which one usually sets out hunting. On the way we talked of the chase.

"Hunting is a question of luck," Osep was saying "Before you know where you are your quarry may vanish into thin air. A novice can easily fail to notice the game. Or, he may get confused, and his hands shake so that he misses. You must fire the moment you catch sight of it. If you waste time lifting your gun to take aim, by the time you've put the butt to your shoulder the game may be far away over the mountain."

"Then how do you go out after game, Master Osep?"

"The clever hunter does not go out after game. He just lies in wait watching for it," the hunter explained. "He knows at what time of day and at what places his quarry will move about, so he goes and lies in wait there. If he does go looking for it, it's not for long, and he moves about in such a way that the game cannot catch his scent. For animals have a strong sense of smell and the moment your quarry catches your scent you've had it: it will take to its heels in a batting of an eyelid."

Thus talking, towards evening we arrived at the cabin of Ovakim the gardener. The old man had gathered wood, built a fire and was now lying beside it.

"Good evening, Master Ovakim."

"Ah, God bless you, an' you're right welcome. Why, my dears, I was just thinking how nice it would be to have someone to talk with. The good Lord must have sent you...." Master Ovakim boomed joyously.

"First tell us, whether there's game or not, Master Ovakim," inquired Osep the hunter impatiently.

"Why, my son, there's a damned stag in these parts. Comes here at night he does, and eats my beans, and goes away at dawn. He's eaten and ruined so many of my beans, he has! You see, I've no gun and no dog. He's a giant of a stag! Has antlers like an oak tree!"

"Never mind. Do the does answer his call?"

"I'll say they do! Why, they don't let me sleep a wink! Last night they made such a racket on the slopes over there that the very ground shook!"

"Praise the Lord!" cried the hunter. Master Ovakim begged us to make ourselves comfortable, spreading soft grass for us to sit upon, and then lay down again by the fire.

"You know, folks, I sometimes think to myself that there's no animal in the world more cruel than man."

"Why, Master Ovakim?"

"Why? Well now, here you are with your guns going after these animals, and we are rejoicing at the thought that we may kill a buck and feast on it. But isn't it a living creature like ourselves? At midnight it cries out with longing and calls to attract its doe.

140

That's how it expresses its love!"

"Let me hear it just once, and I'll show it love!" Osep chuckled.

"No, it's sinful that's what it is," said Ovakim shaking his head. Then raising his voice he went on:

"Since we're on the subject of stags, my lads, let me tell you a story."

"Come on, let's hear it, Master Ovakim!" we chorused.

"In the mountains one year, news was brought to me that my grandson had fallen ill and was asking for me. He wanted very much to see me. So I started down homewards. I went a bit out of my way to see if I could find some game to take home with me. I'd been looking about for a while when I noticed something rustling in the brushwood, and a bush shaking. It didn't seem to be a bird. But if it was a beast, why didn't it show itself? I threw a stone into the bush. The ears of a young buck popped up and dropped out of sight again, and the bush shook as it struggled to open a passage and make off. I raised my gun and aimed it at the heaving bush. As the shot rang out the buck sprang forth and crashed to the ground. Well, lads, it began squealing and moaning just like a dying child. From the tales of master hunters I knew that its mother must have seen me and hidden nearby, and that hearing its moans, she would be back at any moment. I hid behind a tree, and watched and waited. After a while she appeared, and what a sight! I wouldn't wish you to see what I saw with my own eyes. Just like a mother, a human mother hearing a gun fired at her child. She came and found her youngster there breathless, sprawling in his blood under the tree. She reached out her muzzle and licked the wound, moaning sadly. I flung my gun over my shoulder and went home. I reached home and found the child in a very grave condition, fighting for breath, and groaning. Folks, that day has passed, but God is my witness! He was moaning just like the young buck. I had only to close my eyes and I thought I was still standing by the bush. In the end the child died. Then his mother bent over him and began moaning piteously. 'O Merciful Lord!' I exclaimed. What is the difference between us and the deer on the mountains?' None at all! A heart is a heart, and grief is grief. . . ."

Under the impression of Master Ovakim's sad story we remained silent for some time.

"Master Ovakim, it is said that bucks have their protectress," said Ghazar the bearer.

"Yes, my boy, and a mighty powerful one!"

"Is that really true?"

"It's true, my boy. Pirum was a master hunter who never missed in his life. Once he wounded a buck, and it took to its heels and he after it. Coming to the edge of Zoravor oak wood, the buck knelt down, and Pirum raised his gun. But just at that moment a door opened into Zoravor oak wood, and a beautiful young woman came out. She stood facing the hunter, and began to scold him.

" 'Why are you pursuing my innocent deer, you wicked man? What has he done to you? May you never have your fill if you don't have enough in this abundant world. May your barrel be blocked with blood, your bullet turn to paste. May the hand wither that holds the gun!'

"Hunter Pirum was a wise man: guessing that she must be the buck's protectress, he threw his gun on to the branch of a tree. And the branch turned dry in the twinkling of an eye."

"Master Ovakim, then they're right in saying that hunting is cursed?"

"It's cursed alright, my boy! Both hunting and fishing, both are cursed. It's an old curse that no hunter or fisherman should ever eat his fill. The minstrel Kyaram also pronounced his curse upon the hunter. As he was looking for his Asli, burning with longing he saw a wounded deer. He found the animal breathing painfully and a calf standing by dismayed. He took up his saz and sang a lay."

We asked Master Ovakim to sing the lay. The old man sang with his aged, cracked voice, by the fire in the dark valley:

"Hey, folks! I saw one verdant spring day,
In these mountains, a handsome doe was a-crying;
A lovely calf stood by dismayed,
In these mountains a handsome doe was a-crying.

"Hit with a bullet it was leaving this vain world,
Sorely lamenting man's senseless cruelty,
Moaning o'er its wound, its blood gushing forth,
In these mountains a handsome doe was a-crying.

For the love of heaven, let none buy meat of game;
For the love of heaven, let none buy meat of game;
For grieved Kyaram saw, in an ocean of blood,
In these mountains, a handsome doe was a-crying."

* * *

Everybody fell asleep, but I remained awake. In such places a stranger cannot sleep at night. He hears a thousand sounds and imagines a thousand things. It must have been the night wind swaying the corn, but to me it seemed the buck described by Master Ovakim was in the garden. In the darkness of the night black figures appeared in the distance and seemed to move.

I just could not sleep.

In the early hours I arose and went to the door. It was a clear autumn night. The dry cold chilled me to the bone. The muffled valleys hissed. They seemed to be asleep, snoring deeply and softly like Master Ovakim.

The morning star was already up and it was time for us to start. I awakened my companions. They hurriedly drew on their boots and we set off towards the Yeghud defile.

* * *

Well before daybreak we were lying in wait in the Yeghud defile. From my post I was watching the open space before me. Beyond it, opposite me, a thick dark forest began.

Gradually the darkness thinned. Frowning rocks peeped sleepily through the mist. The sky grew pale and clear. Then the dawn came. The early morning breeze stirred. The flowers moved their heads, the grass trembled, and the leaves rustled. The forest began to awake. A bird called from a nearby tree, a second from another and a third from a distant one.

Unawares, I had broken cover and was standing in the open gazing around rapturously at nature, at the sacred hour when the first light of day is born.

Suddenly there was a sound...a dry branch cracked in the forest. I turned to look. The forest was still dark and I could see nothing, but I could hear cautious steps approaching over dry leaves...crunch...crunch ...crunch. Nothing was yet visible, but again I heard it—crunch...crunch...crunch coming nearer and nearer.... There! There it was!

It was the first time in my life I had seen a deer in its natural state. It came out with a calm pride, regal and superb like the lord and king of all the beauties of nature. Half of it still hidden in the darkness of the forest, it lowered its brown muzzle to the ground, then raising its head it swung its neck with a wild grace and looked towards me.

144

It was the most beautiful gaze I have ever seen in my life.

I was embarrassed, ashamed and wanted to hide my gun. But no sooner had I made the slightest motion than it suddenly turned away its swan-like neck. Osep's gun roared forth from the neighboring covert. The report rumbled through the forest. And the bushes began to crack. The buck was running away.

"A plague on you!" Osep cursed me as he jumped out from his covert and ran to a near-by mound to see where the buck would appear. The morning was brightening and there was light enough for us to find the marks of fresh blood on the green grass.

The buck was wounded. We followed the trail of blood to find it.

"If it has lost so much blood, let it run as much as it likes. It's ours," said Osep the hunter.

* * *

Towards evening we found it in a forest thicket. From its lying position it stretched up its long neck towards us. I saw that it could barely hold its head up. It stared at us through dim, half-closed, unseeing eyes. It seemed to have suddenly understood. It tried to get up, but rising to its knees it fell back with a splash into its blood with a powerless groan.

The hunter ran up. . . . I wanted to say something but I was ashamed. He got hold of the buck's head and twisted the beautiful neck. Again I wanted to intervene. . . . Again I lost heart. . . . There, the dagger glittered.

I turned my face away as if looking at the mountains. I heard a dull groan from behind. . . . And I don't know why, I began to think about life and death, and how ugly life seemed to me!

1909

TALES

NAZAR THE BRAVE

1

ONCE UPON A TIME there lived a peasant whose name was Nazar. He was lazy, good-for-nothing, and cowardly, so cowardly that he was afraid to take a single step by himself. He was always hanging on to his wife's skirts; wherever she went, he would follow her. And people nicknamed him Nazar the Coward.

One night Nazar the Coward followed his wife out of doors. He stood outside the door, and seeing everything around lit up by bright moonlight, said:

"There's a night for you! Makes me long to attack and rob the caravan that goes from Hindustan to the Shah's city and fill our house wth riches!"

"Be quiet, you fool! To think of a coward like you even daring to speak of robbing caravans! Get back to bed and stay there!"

Nazar began to scold her.

"That's just like you, you foolish woman! Now you're preventing me from robbing the Shah's caravan and filling our house with riches! Am I a man or aren't I? How dare you argue with me!"

Seeing his temper was up and he would not calm down, his wife ran back into the house and locked the door.

"Go on, rob the Shah's caravan, if you can, old chicken-heart!" she sneered.

Shut out in the yard, Nazar stood with his heart in his mouth.

"Let me in! Please, let me in!" he begged.

But she wouldn't. He pleaded with her in vain for some time. Finally he gave up, and squatted against a wall and waited shivering until morning.

The night passed and morning came, and Nazar lay dozing disconsolately in the sun, waiting for his wife to let him in. It was summer and there were flies everywhere. They settled on Nazar's face in swarms. At first he was too lazy to make the effort to raise a hand and swat them, but in the end he could bear it no longer, and slapped his forehead. Dead flies dropped all around him.

"Aha!" muttered Nazar, "how many of them have I killed, I wonder?"

He began to count the dead flies, but soon lost count.

"Anyway, there must be at least a thousand," he mused. "Never knew I had it in me! If I can kill a thousand creatures with a single blow, I'm sure I can get on without my wife!"

He got up and went straight to see the village priest.

"Father, give me your blessing."

"God bless you, my son," said the priest.

"It's like this, father," Nazar began and went on to tell the priest about his feat, adding that he must leave his wife, and asking the priest to write down his feat so that it would not remain unknown and everyone might read and know about it.

As a joke, the priest wrote down on an old rag:

"Nazar the Brave, who fear does not know,
Kills a thousand with a single blow!"

He gave the rag to Nazar, who fixed it to a long pole, buckled on a rusty old sabre, mounted his donkey and rode out of the village.

2

Nazar rode along, not knowing where he was going. After a while he looked back and saw that the village lay far behind and was afraid again. He began to hum, sing, talk to himself and shout at the donkey, just to keep his courage up. He shouted louder and louder, and finally the donkey began to bray in answer. On they went, the one shouting and the other braying louder and louder. All who heard them were scared. The birds flew away, the hares scampered into the forest, and the frogs jumped croaking into the water.

But when they rode into the forest Nazar was even more afraid than before. It seemed to him that there was a wild animal or a robber lurking behind every bush and tree, ready to pounce on him. He now began to yell as loud as he possibly could, enough to strike fear into the heart of anyone who might hear.

And, indeed, it so happened that a peasant from a neighboring village was walking along the road towards them through the forest, leading his horse by the reins. When he heard the terrific din, he began to quake and crying, "Woe is me! Robbers!" ran to hide in the woods, leaving his horse on the road.

Nazar reached the spot where the man left his horse and saw the riderless horse standing there all saddled and bridled. What more could he have wanted? He straightway dismounted from his donkey, climbed onto the horse and rode away.

3

How far Nazar rode on, whether a long way or a short way, is only known to himself, but at length he came to a village. He had never been there before, and knew not where to go. Suddenly he heard music. Riding towards it, he found many people gathered for a wedding feast.

"Greetings!"

"Greetings to you, stranger! Take a seat of honor, and be our guest."

They seated Nazar at the place of honor, and brought him vast quantities of wine and food. The guests wondered who he could be. The man sitting on his right nudged his neighbor, who nudged the next man, and so the nudging passed all around the table until it came to the priest, who sat to the left of Nazar.

The priest looked at Nazar's "banner," and spelled out.

"Nazar the Brave, who fear does not know,
Kills a thousand with a single blow!"

The priest whispered this in awe to the man on his left, who whispered it to his neighbor, and so it went back around the table until it reached the guest sitting on Nazar's right.

All were greatly impressed when they learned that their guest was no less than,

"Nazar the Brave, who fear does not know,
Kills a thousand with a single blow!"

Suddenly one of the guests, who was known as a boaster, exclaimed: "Why, of course! It's Nazar the Brave! How he has changed. I hardly recognized him."

Many of the others then began to remember Nazar the Brave, and tell stories of the great feats he had performed, not omitting to mention how long they had known him and the days they had spent together with him.

"How can such a great man travel without servants?" asked some people dubiously.

"Why, that's the way he is. He doesn't like to keep servants. He says, 'Why should I have servants, when the whole world serves me?' "

"Why does he carry such a rusty old sword?"

"Why, that just shows his bravery. With a good sword at his side, anyone can be brave enough, but Nazar kills a thousand with a single blow of that rusty old sword of his!"

All the guests drank to the health of Nazar the Brave, and one of the most important men present made a speech.

"The fame of your feats reached us long ago, O Nazar the Brave! And we are honored to have you with us today!"

Nazar merely sighed, and waved his hand. The guests exchanged meaningful glances to show they understood the deep significance of that sigh and wave of the hand.

Then the ashoogh rose, and sang a song in his honor.

"Welcome to thee! We hail thy might,
O great eagle of our mountain heights!
Crown and glory of our land, our light!
Nazar the Brave, who fear does not know,
Kills a thousand with a single blow!

"Champion of the weak, healer of the sick,
Our saviour from pain, woe and foul trick,
You defend from injustice the humble and meek!
Nazar the Brave, who fear does not know,
Kills a thousand with a single blow!

"As lambs of the sacrifice we'll be to you,
To your banner, your saber and to your horse too,
And to its mane and its tail and its shoe!
Nazar the Brave who fear does not know,
Kills a thousand with a single blow!"

And as the drunken guests dispersed, they chanted wherever they went,

"Nazar the Brave who fear does not know,
Kills a thousand with a single blow!"

They told of his remarkable exploits and described his fierce appearance. And people began to name their newborn Nazar.

4

Nazar left the wedding feast and continued on his way. Coming to a green meadow, he dismounted, set his horse loose to graze, stuck his flag in the ground, and lay down to sleep under it.

Now it so happened that in a castle on the top of a neighboring mountain there lived seven Giant warrior brothers. Looking down from their castle, they were amazed to see someone sleeping in their field.

"Who can be so brave and strong as to dare to trespass on our land, and even sleep on it?" they wondered. And taking their enormous clubs they went down to the field to see who the trespasser could be. They arrived to find a horse grazing, and a man asleep on the ground beneath a banner, bearing the words:

"Nazar the Brave, who fear does not know,
Kills a thousand with a single blow!"

"Aha! So it's Nazar the Brave himself!" they exclaimed in awed tones, for the news spread by the drunken wedding guests had travelled this far. And they stood rooted to the spot, waiting for Nazar to awaken.

When Nazar woke up and saw the seven Giants standing over him with their enormous clubs, he nearly died of fright, and tried to hide behind the pole of his banner. Seeing him pale and quivering the Giants thought he was enraged and about to finish them all off with one fell blow, so they fell to their knees, crying:

"O Nazar the Brave, who knows no fear! We have heard such a lot about you, and we are indeed honored by your visit. Our castle is on yonder mountain. We have a very beautiful sister who lives there with us. We beg you to come to our castle and be our guest!"

Nazar recovered his wits and mounted his horse, and the seven Giants, carrying his banner, escorted him to their castle.

There they received him with great honors, and so extolled his courage and manly virtues that their sister, the beautiful Iar, straightaway fell in love with him. Nazar's star was certainly in the ascendant, and the honor and respect in which he was held continued to increase.

5

At that time a great savage tiger appeared in the region. Everybody in the neighborhood was terrified, and people asked each other, "Who will rid us of this terrible tiger? Why, Nazar the Brave, of course. Who else will dare face the beast?"

All eyes were turned to Nazar; as God was in heaven, so was Nazar the Brave on earth.

When Nazar heard the word "tiger," he was so scared that he ran away, his one idea to get home as fast as his legs would carry him. But everyone decided he had run off to kill the tiger with his bare hands, and his beautiful bride called after him:

"Stop, stop, my hero! Do not go unarmed!"

Weapons were brought out to him, and armed to

the teeth, Nazar mounted his horse and galloped away. He didn't know or care where he went; all he wanted was to get as far away as possible. Coming to a forest, he sprang from his horse and climbed a tree, thinking he would be safer there. He clung to a bough, more dead than alive from terror, his heart pounding wildly. As luck would have it, the tiger came along and lay down under that very tree. When Nazar saw the tiger, his blood froze, and everything went dark before his eyes. His arms grew weak, and he lost his grip and came crashing down right onto the tiger's back. The beast was so surprised that it jumped up in panic and raced away over hills and vales, with Nazar clinging on to its back for dear life. The people who saw them cried:

"See! Nazar the Brave has tamed the tiger, and is riding it like a horse!"

They all grabbed their daggers, their guns, and their swords, and ran down and killed the tiger.

Recovering his wits Nazar found his tongue again and said:

"What a pity you killed the beast! I had just tamed him. I wanted to use him instead of a horse."

The news spread far and wide in no time at all, and they gave him a great reception in the castle. They sang an ode to his glory which ran:

"In all creation
In any nation
Who's your equal, who's not your slave
O Nazar the Brave?

"A fork of lightning
A hawk striking
You darted down our people to save
O Nazar the Brave!

"A tiger you coursed
As though t'were a horse
And rode on its back o'er hill and o'er vale
O Nazar the Brave!

"A saviour! You freed us!
O saviour! Now heed us!
Forever we'll praise thee, forever to save!
O Nazar the Brave!"

Nazar the Brave married the Giants' sister, and the
wedding feast lasted for seven days and seven nights.
Songs were sung in his praise, and in praise of his
bride.

"The moon arose behind the hill.
Whom does it resemble?
The moon arose behind the hill.
It's Nazar the Brave himself!

"The sun arose in all its glory.
Whom does it resemble?
The sun arose in all its glory.
It's Nazar the Brave's fair bride.
"Lo, our noble king so fair!
Lo, his shining sun so fair!
His crown is bright—brightest bright!
His robes are bright—brightest bright!
His belt is bright—brightest bright!
His boots are bright—brightest bright!
His Queen is bright—brightest bright!
We bow down to thee bright Queen,
O sun of the most bright King!
We pay homage to thee—all hail!
"Nazar the Brave! All hail! All hail!

And thee fair Queen—All hail! All hail!
And the whole wide world—All hail! All hail!"

That wasn't all.

It so happened that the King of the neighboring country had wanted to marry the Giants' sister himself, and when he heard that the Giants had given her in marriage to Nazar, he declared war on them and sent out his armies to attack their castle.

The Giants came to Nazar and told him about the war. Then bowing low, they stood before him, awaiting his command.

As soon as Nazar heard the word "war," he dashed out of the castle, his one idea to get back home as fast as his legs would carry him. Everybody thought he wanted to attack the enemy single-handedly and unarmed, and barred his way, begging him to stop, and arm himself first.

Weapons were brought, while his wife implored her brothers not to let him go out and engage the enemy army single-handedly. The news that Nazar the Brave had wanted to attack the enemy single-handedly and unarmed had already spread everywhere. The whole people and the army had heard and scouts had brought word of it to the enemy forces. Now he was reported to have set out surrounded by the seven Giants.

On reaching the battlefield he was made to mount a large black charger, and all the soldiers shouted:

"Long live Nazar the Brave! Death to the enemy!"

The charger felt that the man on his back was a pretty poor horseman, so he took the bit in his teeth and bolted straight for the enemy lines. The Giants and all their warriors thought that Nazar was charging the enemy without waiting for support, and charged after him with triumphant cries. Unable to restrain his steed, Nazar reached out and clutched the branch of a tree as he galloped past, hoping to swing himself out of the saddle. But the tree happened to be dry and rotten, and the branch broke off, and there he was, galloping towards the enemy with an enormous branch in his hands.

When the enemy saw this, demoralized as they were by his great renown, they turned and fled, crying, "Run for your lives; Nazar the Brave is charging us, tearing up trees by the roots as he comes!"

Many of the enemy were slaughtered that day and those who remained alive lay down their arms at Nazar's feet and swore allegiance to him.

Nazar the Brave was escorted back to the Giants' castle amid great rejoicing. The people erected triumphal arches in his honor and gave him a tumultuous welcome, with cries of "hurrah" and "long live Nazar the Brave," music and singing, and countless speeches, so that Nazar was quite overwhelmed by it all.

After this great victory, Nazar was proclaimed King, and mounted the throne amid great pomp and ceremony. The seven Giants were appointed as his advisers. And he saw that the world was at his feet.

They say that Nazar the Brave still reigns there to this day. And when people speak of valor, intelligence or talent in his presence, he laughs and says:

"What valor!? What intelligence!? What talent!? These are all empty words. It's a question of luck. If you're lucky—make merry!"

And they say that to this day Nazar the Brave is making merry and laughing at the whole world.

1908

THE LIAR

ONCE UPON A TIME there lived a king. This king announced throughout the land:

"I shall give half my kingdom to the man who can tell a lie that I admit to be a lie."

A shepherd came and said, "Lond may Your Majesty Reign! My father had a cudgel which he used to reach out from here and stir the stars in the sky."

"That's possible," answered the King. "My grandfather had a pipe. He used to put one end of it in his mouth and stretch the other up to the sun to light it."

The man went out scratching his head.

A tailor came and said, "I am sorry, O King, to have come so late. I had intended to come earlier. But there was a heavy storm yesterday, and lightning rent the sky. I've been patching it up."

"Oh, very commendable," said the King, "but you haven't patched it very well, for it rained a little again this morning."

This man also went away empty-handed.

A peasant came in with a bag on his shoulder.

"What do you want, my good man?" asked the King.

"You owe me a bag of gold. I have come for it."

"A bag of gold!" exclaimed the King astonished. "That's a lie. I do not owe you anything."

"All right. It is a lie. Then give me half your kingdom."

"No, no. You're quite right. It's not a lie," the king tried to correct himself.

"So I am telling the truth. Then give me the bag of gold."

1907

160

THE SPARROW

ONCE THERE WAS a sparrow that got a thorn in its foot. It flew here and there until it came across an old woman looking for firewood to heat her oven and bake some bread.

"Granny, Granny," said the sparrow, "pull this thorn out of my foot. Then make your fire and I'll go peck-pecking not to starve."

The old woman pulled the thorn out and built her oven fire.

The sparrow hopped off a little way, then returned and told the old woman to give it back its thorn.

"I have dropped the thorn into the oven fire," she said.

The sparrow insisted, "Give me back my thorn or I'll fly off with a loaf." The old woman gave the sparrow a loaf, and it flew away.

A short while later it came across a shepherd drinking his milk without bread.

"Shepherd, shepherd," it said. "Why are you having your milk without bread? Here, take this loaf, crumble it in your milk and eat, and I'll go peck-pecking not to starve."

The sparrow hopped off a little way, then returned and told the shepherd to give it back its loaf of bread.

"I have eaten it," said the shepherd.

"Give me back my loaf of bread," insisted the sparrow, "or I'll fly off with a lamb from your flock."

The shepherd gave the sparrow a lamb and it flew away.

A short while later it came across some people who were celebrating a wedding but had no cattle to slaughter.

"Don't worry," it said, "here, take my lamb, kill it and prepare a feast, and I'll go peck-pecking not to starve."

The sparrow hopped off a little way, then returned and demanded the lamb back.

"We have killed and eaten it," said the people. "How can we return it?"

"Give me back my lamb," insisted the sparrow, "or I'll fly off with the bride."

And it snatched up the bride and flew away. It flew and flew until it came across a minstrel walking along a road.

"Minstrel, minstrel," it said. "Take this bride and keep her and I'll go peck-pecking not to starve."

The sparrow hopped off a little way, then returned and demanded the bride back.

"But the bride has gone home to her love," said the minstrel.

"Give me back my bride," insisted the sparrow, "or I'll fly off with your saz."

The minstrel gave the sparrow his saz, and it slung it over its shoulder and flew away.

Then it perched on a branch and began to twang and chirp thus:

"Twang, twing, twang,
I traded a thorn for a loaf,
I bartered the loaf for a lamb,
I exchanged the lamb for a bride,
I swapped the bride for a saz,
I got the saz and became a minstrel,
Twang, twing, twang."

1907

THE MASTER AND THE LABORER

ONCE UPON A TIME there lived two brothers, both very poor. They decided that the older of the two should find work as a laborer for some rich landowner, and send his earnings home.

The younger brother stayed at home, and the elder went and hired himself to a rich master.

The agreement was that he should work until spring, until the first cuckoo called, but the master added a clause:

"If either of us gets angry with the other before then, he will pay a fine. If you get angry with me, you will pay me a thousand rubles. If I get angry with you, I shall pay you a thousand rubles."

"But I don't have the money!" exclaimed the laborer.

"That doesn't matter. If you lose, you'll stay on and work for me ten years without pay!"

At first the laborer wanted to refuse, but then he thought:

"After all, I can control myself and never get angry. If the master loses his temper, he'll have to pay me a thousand rubles. What can I lose?"

He accepted.

Early the next morning the master sent him to work in the fields.

"Take a scythe, and mow as long as there is light," he said.

The laborer toiled in the field all day long, and

returned home in the evening completely worn out. The master said to him:

"Why have you come home so early?"

"What do you mean? The sun has set!"

"Well, and what of it? Didn't I tell you to work as long as there's light? The sun has gone down, but the moon is up, and there's quite enough light to work by."

"Do you mean I can never rest?" cried the laborer.

"Aha—you are getting angry!"

"No, no, not at all.... Only I'm very tried.... I'll just rest a bit, and then go out to the field again."

He worked all night until the moon went down. But then the sun came up again. The poor man sank down exhausted. He began to curse his master.

"Curse your field, and your bread, and your money," he cried.

At that moment the master came up to him, and said:

"So you are angry! Don't forget our agreement. Now you either pay me a thousand rubles, or you work for me without pay for ten years."

The laborer didn't know what to do. He had no money, but he couldn't go on working for such a harsh master. Finally he signed a paper stating he owed the master a thousand rubles, and went home empty-handed.

His younger brother asked him what had happened, and he told the whole story.

"That's nothing. Don't worry," said the younger brother. "Now you stay at home, and I'll go and find work."

He went to the same master his brother had worked for.

The master offered him the same conditions. If the

laborer got angry, he was to pay the master a thousand rubles, or work ten years without pay. If the master got angry, he was to pay the laborer a thousand rubles, and let him go free.

"No, that's not enough," said the younger brother. "Let's make it two thousand rubles you pay me if you get angry, and two thousand rubles I pay you if I get angry—or work twenty years for you without pay!"

"Agreed!" cried the master eagerly, and took the man into his service.

The next morning the sun was already high, but the master found the laborer still fast asleep.

"Get up this minute! It's nearly noon, and you're not at work yet!"

"Are you angry?" asked the laborer, suddenly opening his eyes.

"No, no—not by any means!" answered the master hastily. "I was merely suggesting it was time for you to start mowing that field."

"Oh, there's time enough for that," replied the laborer lazily.

Finally he got up and began leisurely pulling on his boots.

"Can't you hurry up a bit?"

"Why, are you getting angry?"

"No, no—I merely wanted to say that you'd be late for work."

"Oh, well, that's different. But remember our agreement—you must carry it out, you know."

By the time the laborer was ready and reached the field, it was nearly noon. "What's the use of working now? It's too late. Look, everybody's having his lunch. Let us eat too," said the laborer.

They sat down and ate. After they had finished, the laborer said. "I'm a working man, I need to have a short nap to keep up my strength." With that he went to sleep and slept until evening.

"Here, wake up! Have you no shame?" cried the master, shaking him. "All the neighbors have finished mowing their fields, while ours stands there untouched! What a fine worker you are!"

"Seems to me you're really angry this time!" said the laborer, raising his head.

"No, no, not at all. I was merely telling you it was time to go home now."

"Well, that's different. Let's go home then."

"When they reached the house, the master found a guest waiting for him. He sent the laborer to kill a sheep so they could prepare a meal for the guest.

"Which sheep shall I kill?" asked the laborer.

"Any you can catch," said the master.

Off the laborer went. Soon afterwards the neighbors came running to the master and said: "Your worker must have gone mad; he's killing all your sheep!"

The master ran out of the house, and saw his entire flock lying there slaughtered.

"What have you done, curse you?" he yelled. "You've ruined me! May the Lord punish you!"

"But you told me yourself to kill any I could catch, and I caught them all!" answered the laborer blandly. "Can it be that you are angry?"

"No, no, not at all. I am merely sorry that you killed all my sheep."

"All right, then. If you are not angry with me, I can go on working for you," said the laborer. He continued to work for a few months, nearly driving his master mad with his tricks. Finally the master decided to get rid of him.

According to the terms of their agreement, the worker was to stay until the first cuckoo called in the forest. The master decided he would make use of this clause. However, winter was only beginning, and it was a long time until the cuckoo would be heard, so he took his wife with him to the woods. He helped her climb a tree, and told her to sit there and call out as a cuckoo would. Then he went home, and told the laborer they would go hunting together in the forest.

As soon as they entered the woods, the master's wife began to call out, "Cuckoo! Cuckoo!" The master turned to the laborer, and said, "Congratulations! There's the first cuckoo and now you are free again!

The laborer saw through the trick.

"No," he said. "How can a cuckoo make itself heard in the beginning of winter? It must be a very strange sort of cuckoo indeed. I'm going to shoot it, and take a good look at it!"

With that he raised his gun and aimed at the tree in which the master's wife was perched.

The master threw himself upon the laborer and tried to wrest the gun from him. "Curse you, you bandit! I can't stand your tricks any longer!"

"Ah, now you'll admit that you really are angry at least," cried the laborer eagerly.

"Yes, yes, I'm angry! I admit it!" said the master. "Come along, I'll give you your two thousand rubles, only go away and leave me in peace. Now I understand the old proverb that says, 'Never dig pitfalls for others, you might fall into them yourself!'"

And the younger brother went home with two thousand rubles in his pocket.

1908

THE DEATH OF KIKOS

ONCE UPON A TIME there lived a poor peasant and his wife, with three daughters.

One day, as the father was working in his field, he felt very thirsty, and sent his eldest daughter to the spring for water. She took a jug and went. Next to the spring grew a large tree.

When she came to the spring, the daughter looked at the tree pensively, and thought:

"One day I'll get married, and have a son whom I'll call Kikos. Kikos will grow up, and one day he'll climb this tree. He'll fall from it, and hit his head on a stone, and be killed. . . . Oh, alas, alas, poor little Kikos!"

She sat down beneath the tree and began to wail, chanting:

> "Some day I'll marry and have a son
> With hair of chestnut brown.
> One day, I know, he'll climb this tree
> And he'll come tumbling down.
> Alas, alas, Kikos dear!
> Alas, dear Kikos is dead!"

She sat there chanting and weeping, and meanwhile everyone at home was wondering why she had not returned. Her mother sent the second daughter to look for her. "Find out what's happened to your sister," she said.

When the eldest daughter saw her sister approaching, she began to wail louder.

"Come quick, you poor unfortunate aunt! See what has happened to your poor little nephew Kikos!"

"What Kikos?"

"Why haven't you heard? Listen."

> "Some day I'll marry and have a son
> With hair of chestnut brown.
> One day, I know he'll climb this tree
> And he'll come tumbling down.
> Alas, alas, Kikos dear!
> Alas, dear Kikos is dead!"

"Alas, dear Kikos is dead!" the second daughter began to wail. She sat down next to her sister, and began to weep.

Meanwhile the mother became still more anxious. She sent out her third daughter. "You better go and see what has happened to your sisters," she said.

The youngest daughter went to the spring, and found her sisters sitting there weeping bitterly.

"What has happened?" she cried anxiously.

"Don't you know?" answered her eldest sister.

> "Some day I'll marry and have a son
> With hair of chestnut brown.
> One day, I know he'll climb this tree
> And he'll come tumbling down.
> Alas, alas, Kikos dear!
> Alas, dear Kikos is dead!"

"Alas, dear Kikos! Why have you left your poor old aunt behind?" wailed the youngest sister, and sat down with the other two. And she too began to weep.

Finally the mother couldn't bear the suspense any

longer, and ran out to the spring herself. All three
daughters ran to meet her.

"Come, quick, you poor unfortunate grandmother!
See what has happened to your dear little grandson!"

"What grandson? And since when am I a grandmother?" cried the amazed woman.

"Why, don't you know yet, Mother?" wailed the
eldest daughter.

"Some day I'll marry and have a son
With hair of chestnut brown.
One day, I know he'll climb this tree
And he'll come tumbling down.
Alas, alas, Kikos dear!
Alas, dear Kikos is dead!"

"Alas, alas! Why am I still living dear Kikos? It
were better that your poor old grandmother should
be dead herself, than to have this happen to you!"
wailed the woman.

The peasant couldn't understand where they had all
gone. He began to look for them, and finally found
them at the spring.

As soon as they saw him coming, they all ran to
meet him, crying.

"Come, quick, you unfortunate grandfather! See
what has happened to your favorite grandson Kikos!"

"Who's a grandfather? Who's Kikos?" asked the
astounded man. "What's this all about, anyway? I
don't understand...."

"What! You don't understand? Haven't you heard?"

"Some day I'll marry and have a son
With hair of chestnut brown.
One day, I know he'll climb this tree
And he'll come tumbling down.

Alas, alas, Kikos dear!
Alas, dear Kikos is dead!"

All four of them wailed in chorus, "Alas, dear Kikos is dead!"

The peasant thought a bit.

"Look here, you foolish women," he said. "Why are you crying? You know you can't bring poor Kikos back to life with your tears. Let us go home instead, and invite the neighbors to a feast in Kikos's memory. Such is life, we come and we depart it."

All they possessed was an ox and a bag of flour. They killed the ox, and baked bread, and invited the guests. Then they ordered a Mass for Kikos's soul, and held a feast in his memory.

That calmed them all, and they went on living as peacefully as before.

1913

THE CARNIVAL

ONCE UPON A TIME there lived a husband and wife who did not see eye to eye. The man called his wife a dim-wit and she returned the compliment. They were always fighting about something or other.

One day, the man bought a hundred pounds of butter and rice, hired a man to carry it on his back and took it home. His wife was furious. "Didn't I always say you were a dim-wit!" she cried. "What did you go and buy so much butter and rice for? Thinking of holding a wedding for your son, for a funeral banquet for your father?"

"What are you talking about? What funeral banquet, what wedding? Take it and put it all away. It's for the Carnival."

The wife calmed down, took the stuff and put it away.

Some time passed and the woman waited and waited, but the Carnival did not come. As she was sitting by the door one day, she saw a man hurrying by along the street. She raised one hand to her forehead and called: "Hey, brother, come here for a minute!"

The young man stopped.

"You're not the Carnival by any chance, are you, brother?" she asked.

The man saw at once that there must be something wrong with her up top and thought to himself:

"Aha, I'll say I am, and see what happens."

"Why, of course, sister. I'm Carnival. What is it?"

"Well, all I have to say is that after all we're not your servants, to keep your rice and butter for such a long time! Aren't you ashamed of yourself, taking advantage of our kindness? Why haven't you ever shown up to take your stuff away?"

"Why so angry, my dear? That's just what I've come for. I've been looking for your house for a long time but couldn't find it."

"Well, alright, come on and take it then."

The man hurried into the house, grabbed the butter and rice, put it on his shoulder and took off for his village.

When the husband came home in the evening, the woman told him: "The Carnival came at last. I gave him back his things and he took them away."

"What Carnival...? What things, Woman?"

"The butter and the rice....I saw him coming along the road, looking for our house. I called him over, gave him a good telling off and had him carry the stuff away on his back."

"Oh, you dim-wit you! You've ruined me! Didn't I always say you were a stupid dim-wit! Which way did he go?"

She showed him and the man mounted his horse and rode after the Carnival.

Meanwhile, the Carnival, making good his escape, glanced back and noticed a man on horseback riding after him. He realized at once that it must be the woman's husband. The man rode up to him and said: "Good day, brother. Have you seen a man going this way?"

"Yes, indeed, I did see one."

"What was he carrying on his back?"

"Butter and rice."

"Ah, he must be the one I'm looking for. Did he go by long ago?"

"Quite a time."

"Do you think I can catch up to him if I ride fast?"

"How could you?" said the Carnival. "You're on horseback, but he was on foot. By the time your horse has taken four steps—one, two, three, four—the man will already have walked away on his two feet: one-two, one-two! Much faster than you!"

"What shall I do then?"

"Well, if you like, you can leave your horse with me and go on foot like him. Maybe then you'll catch up to him."

"Yes, yes, well said!" approved the dim-witted man. And he climbed off his horse, left it with the other man, and set off on foot—one-two, one-two.... As soon as he was out of sight the Carnival loaded his burden on the horse's back, turned off the road and galloped home.

Our man, however, walked on and on and finding nobody turned around and came back—to find both the horse and the stranger gone. He returned home and husband and wife started fighting anew: the man because of the butter and rice, the woman because of the horse. And they are fighting to this day. He calls her a dim-wit, and she returns the compliment.

And the Carnival listens and laughs to himself.
1911

THE HANDLESS GIRL

ONCE UPON A TIME, long, long ago there lived a brother and a sister. The sister was passing fair, as lovely to behold as a ray of light, and her name was Lusig, which in Armenian indeed means a lovely ray of light.

The brother married and brought his wife home.

The wife saw that everyone loved Lusig and her heart was gripped by jealousy. She began to gossip about Lusig, and made her cry almost every day.

The brother tried to keep his sister happy when he came home, and would bring her flowers, or a new dress, or some other gift.

And Lusig lived on happily, and kept her beauty, and everybody loved her.

The sister-in-law was so jealous she was beside herself with anger. She wondered what she could do to get rid of Lusig.

One day when her husband left for work, she turned all the furniture upside down, broke all the crockery and kitchen utensils, and then stood in the doorway with folded arms and waited for her husband's return.

When she saw him coming, she began to lament, "Alas! Alack! Everything we had this lovely sister of yours has destroyed!"

" 'Tis of no matter, dear wife, why do you weep so? All these things we can buy. If it is a dish that is broken we can replace it. But if we break Lusig's heart, we shall find it hard to make a new one."

The wife saw that her evil scheme had failed. Another day when her husband went out, she took his favorite horse and drove it far away into the fields, and then stood in the doorway with folded arms and waited for her husband's return.

"Alas! This loving sister of yours took your favorite horse and lost him in the fields. She is simply trying to destroy our home." " 'Tis nothing," said the husband. "It is only a horse. If it is lost, I can work and buy another, but you know I cannot get another sister."

When the wicked wife saw that this plan had also failed, she got even angrier.

One night she slew her baby in its cradle, and put the blood-stained knife among Lusig's clothes. Then she tore her hair, and wailed, "Alas! My little child, my sweet innocent child...." The brother and sister awoke and saw that the baby had been slain in its cradle. They were horrified and heart-broken. But who could have done such a terrible thing?

"Who could it be?" The wife demanded. "No one has been in the house. Let us search and see in whose clothes we find the bloody knife. If we find it, then we have found the culprit."

They agreed, and looking all around, finally found the knife in Lusig's clothes. It was unbelievable, but there it was.

"And this is your beloved sister!" cried the wicked wife and clawed her face, and tore her hair, and wailed, "My child, my sweet only child...."

In the morning the news spread throughout the land. The people were outraged, and demanded that Lusig be punished. The mother wept and demanded justice, and the fair Lusig was sent to prison. At the trial the judge ordered that her hands be cut off.

Later they took her to a distant wood and left her

there alone.

Lusig walked along in the wilderness. In her restless wandering the plants and bushes tore her clothes to shreds, until she was almost naked. The bees stung her, mosquitos bit her, and she had no hands to drive them away. In the end she hid herself in a hollow tree.

It happened that at that time the King's son was hunting in the woods. The dogs ran this way and that and finally surrounded the tree in which Lusig was hiding and began to howl.

The King's son and his men thought the dogs must have discovered a wild beast, and began to urge them to drive the animal out.

"Don't set the dogs on me, my lord," cried the maiden from the hollow tree, "I am a human being, not an animal."

"If you are human, come forth," said the prince.

"I can't for I am naked and am ashamed."

The prince jumped down from his horse took off his cloak and gave it to his men to carry to the tree. A lovely maiden walked out. She was so remarkably beautiful that a man could have no mind to eat or drink when he could feast his eyes on such a beautiful creature. The prince was enchanted. "Who are you, fairest maid? And why did you hide in this hollow tree?"

"I'm just a girl who is all alone. At home I had a brother, but he and his wife have cast me out."

"I shall not abandon you in your plight," said the prince. He brought Lusig home, and told his parents that he loved her, and that they should prepare a splendid wedding.

"If you refuse to let me marry her," he said, "I may well do something rash."

"My son," pleaded the Queen, "there are many beautiful maidens, daughters of kings, ministers, and envoys. They're all rich and beautiful. Why should you wed this girl who hasn't even got hands, and no home or even clothes!"

"Oh, no, mother, this is the only girl I will love."

The King and Queen summoned the wise men of the land and asked their advice. Should they let their son marry this handless girl or not?

The wise men said that the love that existed between a man and a wife was born in their hearts. "It seems to us that the love of your son is for that girl, for his heart is burning for her. God has seen that there is good in their union."

When the King and Queen heard this advice, they both agreed to their son's marriage to Lusig. The wedding feast lasted seven days and seven nights, and the prince had the beautiful Lusig for his wife.

Some time later the prince went away to distant lands. During his absence Lusig bore a beautiful boy with golden hair.

The King and Queen were as overjoyed as though the whole world had been given to them. They wrote a happy letter and gave it to a messenger to take to their son. Now, while on his way this messenger stopped off at Lusig's brother's home, and happened to spend the night as a guest there. While he was chatting with the man and his wife, the messenger told them of the events at court and how he was carrying glad tidings to the prince.

The wicked sister-in-law at once understood what had happened. At midnight she arose, took the letter from the messenger's pocket, threw it into the fire, and wrote a new one which she slipped into the messenger's pocket. This letter said: "After you left home, your wife gave birth to a monster. We are dishonored before the people and the whole world. Please write and tell us what we should do."

The messenger took this letter and delivered it to the prince. When the prince read it he was overcome with grief. He wrote to his parents: "Probably such is my fate. Whatever God has given to me is mine. Don't say any bitter words to my wife. Wait for my return."

He gave the letter to the messenger and sent him back. On the way the messenger again passed the night in the same house.

The wicked sister-in-law again arose at midnight, read the letter and destroyed it. In its place she put a new one she had written, which said: "Whatever my wife has borne, tie it to her breast and drive her out, so that when I come back, I won't have to see her. If you do anything contrary to my will, it may lead to disaster."

When the King and Queen got the letter, they felt very sorry for their daughter-in-law and grandchild. But they felt they must do as their son had instructed.

So they tied the baby to its mother's breast, blessed them weeping, and drove them out of the palace.

The grief-stricken mother wept as she wandered on with her baby. She passed many fords, dark woods, and wildernesses and then came to an arid desert.

In the desert she walked on and on hungry and thirsty, until finally she reached a well. She looked into the water, and it seemed very close, but as she leaned forward to drink, the baby fell into the well. She rushed this way and that around the well crying bitterly when suddenly she heard a voice behind her saying: "Don't be afraid, my dear girl, don't be afraid, my dear. Reach down and rescue it."

Turning, she saw an old man whose white beard reached down to his belt. "How can I rescue my baby, dear father!" she cried. "I have no hands."

"Take him out, take him out. You have hands, reach down."

Lusig reached down and—lo and behold—she had hands, and lifted the baby out of the well. When she turned round to thank the old man, she found that he had disappeared.

In the meantime, the prince had returned home and learned all that had happened in his absence. He refused to enter his father's palace, and instead went searching everywhere for his wife and child, questioning people at every step.

One day he met a man.

"Good day," he said.

"God's blessing on you," answered the stranger.

"Where are you going?"

"I am looking for my sister."

"And I am looking for my wife and child. Let us go together in our search."

The two set off together. They wandered one year, two years, three years, and still did not find their lost ones, or learn any news of them. Finally the prince put up at an inn, and his companion went to fetch his wife. He brought her and their belongings to the inn, and they lived there together, hoping to get some news from the inn-keeper, or his guests.

One day a poor woman came there with her little boy. The prince said to his companion, "Let us talk to this poor woman and her boy. These people know good tales, and tell them well. We men of sorrow will listen to them and the night will pass quickly."

The companion's wife rejected the idea, saying that they had just established themselves there with their belongings, and how could they find a place for this stranger and her child.

However, at the prince's insistence they took in the beggar woman and her son. The mother sat sadly against the wall with her son at her side.

The King's son said, "We cannot sleep, sister. Perhaps you know some legends or tales. Tell us what you know, and we will listen to you and the night will pass quickly."

The poor woman said.

"I know a true story which happened in our lifetime, and is very interesting. I will tell it to you if you wish."

"Good, tell us your story."

The poor woman began her tale.

"In our time there lived a brother and sister. The brother married and brought home a very wicked wife."

The wife of the prince's companion was extremely displeased and exclaimed angrily, "What a story!"

"What's the matter with you? Why do you spoil her story? Come, let her speak," the man chided his wife, and turning to the poor woman added, "We'll listen to you, sister. Go ahead and tell your story."

The poor woman continued.

"The sister was a kind-hearted girl, and everybody loved her. Every time her brother came home, he brought her something—flowers, fruit or a dress, and he always had a kind word for her. The sister-in-law became jealous and took to inventing schemes to get rid of the beautiful girl."

"What a stupid story!" the wife interrupted again.

"What's the matter with you? Let us hear her out, and see what she has to say. Continue, dear sister, don't pay any attention to her."

The poor woman continued.

"The wicked sister-in-law thought up many evil schemes: one day she destroyed all the furniture and crockery in the house and blamed it onto the girl. Another day she let her husband's horse run away, and again put the blame on his sister. When she saw that this scheme had also failed, she murdered her own

181

baby in its cradle, and put the knife among the girl's clothes. . . ."

"Be silent, you shameless hussy! Who ever heard of a mother murdering her baby?" the wife interrupted angrily.

"Why do you keep interrupting?" the man shouted at his wife. "Let her tell her story. Don't you see what an interesting tale she's telling us?"

The poor woman continued:

"They took the case to court. They cut off the hands of the innocent girl, and left her helpless in a far away land. She wandered through the woods in a desperate condition, until one day the King's son happened to be hunting in the forest, and found this beautiful girl and married her. After a time the King's son left for a foreign land. While he was away, his wife bore a golden-haired child. The King and Queen wrote the glad tidings to their son. On the way the messenger chanced to stop at the home of the handless girl's brother. During the night while everyone was asleep, the wicked sister-in-law destroyed the letter and wrote a new one to the King's son, saying that his wife had given birth to a monster. . . ."

"Cut your story short, you have said foolish things enough. I don't want to hear any more or even see your face!" the wife shouted angrily.

"Brother, tell your wife to keep quiet. Let us hear her out. You see what an interesting tale she tells," begged the prince.

The poor woman continued:

"The King's son was grief-stricken when he read the letter, yet he wrote to his parents that they should keep her and the child until he returned. On the way back, the messenger again stopped at the same house. The wicked sister-in-law once again changed the letter, and wrote: "As soon as you receive my letter, tie the child to its mother's breast and drive them out." When the parents received the letter, although they pitied the mother and the lovely child, they obeyed their son's instructions and threw out both the mother and the baby."

"Whence did this bitch come to our house?" cried the wife.

"That's enough!" shouted both the husband and the prince. "Go on, sister...then what happened?"

The poor woman resumed:

"Later the King's son came home, heard what had happened, and set out to look for his wife and son. On the way, he chanced to meet the brother of the handless girl who was searching for his sister. They continued their search together, but neither could find the one he was looking for. Finally they came to a large roadside inn."

"She's a liar!" cried the wife.

The man and the King's son waited breathlessly to hear the end.

And the poor woman finished her story thus:

"Hungry and in rags the woman tramped around with her golden-haired boy. In the end, tired and thirsty, she came to the door of the roadside inn. The brother and husband took pity on her, invited her in and asked her to tell them a story."

The wife began to scream hysterically.

"My dearest Lusig, can it be you....?" burst out the King's son.

"Dear, sweet Lusig, is it you?" cried his companion.

"Yes, I am Lusig, here is my brother, here is my husband, here is my golden curly-haired boy, and here is the wicked sister-in-law."

Their joy was beyond description. After all their long searching, they had finally found each other.

They tied the wicked sister-in-law to the tail of a

mad horse, and turned him loose in the fields. Where-ever the blood dripped there grew thorns and briars; where tears dropped, lakes formed, in the depths of which appeared a baby asleep in its cradle, a knife beneath the pillow.

It is said that there is also a monastery in that region and that in that monastery a woman kneels, and weeps and weeps, endlessly.

THE TALKING FISH

ONCE UPON A TIME there was a poor man who worked for a fisherman, in return for a few fish a day. This was all he and his wife had to live on.

One day the fisherman caught a very pretty little fish, and telling his help to put it away, waded back out in the river. As he turned it over in his hands, the man thought:

"Poor little fish! After all, it's a living creature too. It must have parents and friends, and it surely has its joys and its sorrows, like we humans do."

Suddenly the fish spoke to him, in a human voice: "See here, brother Man! I was playing with my companions so happily that I forgot to be careful and got caught in your net. Now my parents and my playmates are probably searching and grieving for me, and here I am, suffering and dying on land! I so want to go back into the river and live and grow in the cool, clear water. Please have pity, and throw me back into the water!" it gasped.

The man pitied the little fish, and threw it back into the water. "All right, my pretty little fish, go along and play again—I don't want your parents to grieve any more!"

The fisherman was furious. "You fool," he cried. "How could you let the fish get away? Begone with you, I don't ever want to see you again. You can die of hunger for all I care."

"What shall I do now?" lamented the poor man, as he trudged sadly homewards.

He was walking along the road plunged in his unhappy thoughts, when suddenly he saw a Monster in human shape coming towards him. The Monster was driving a very fine cow before him.

"Good day, brother," said the Monster. "Why do you look so sad?"

The man told him his story, and lamented that he didn't know how he was going to earn a living or how he was going to break the news to his wife.

"See here, my friend," said the Monster. "You see this cow? I'll let you have her for three years. She'll give you a lot of good milk every day, and you and your wife will never go hungry. But only on this condition: when three years have passed, I will come and ask you some questions. If you can answer them, the cow will be yours. But if you can't, then I'll take both of you along with the cow, and do whatever I want with you. Do you accept?"

The man thought a bit. "Better to take the cow than go hungry. We'll be able to live for three years, and then we'll see what happens. Perhaps we'll be lucky, and be able to answer those questions." He accepted, took the cow and went home happily.

The three years passed quickly. The cow gave enough milk to feed the poor man and his wife.

Yet they would both sit at their door in the evenings, thinking that soon the Monster would come for them. They sighed and worried about it, while the fateful night came closer and closer.

One evening, as they sat there, a very handsome youth came up to them.

"Good evening," he said. "I'm very tired, and it's getting late. May I spend the night under your roof?"

"Of course you may, only tonight something terrible

186

is going to happen to us! We took a cow from a Monster, on the condition that if we used its milk for three years, he could come and ask us questions at the end of that time, which is tonight. If we answer those questions, then the cow is to be ours, but if we can't, then we will become the Monster's prisoners. So take care that no harm comes to you."

"That doesn't matter. Whatever happens to you, will happen to me too," said the youth, and stayed there with them.

On the stroke of midnight there came a loud knocking at the door.

"Who's there?"

"It's me, the Monster! Three years have passed. Now answer my questions!"

"We'll never be able to answer them," wailed the poor man and his wife.

But the youth said to them, "Don't worry, I'll answer for you," and he went to the door.

"I'm here, waiting," growled the Monster outside.

"And I'm here too," the youth answered calmly from behind the door.

"Where are you from?"

"From over the Sea!"

"How did you get here?"

"Riding a lame flea!"

"Then the Sea must have been very small?"

"Not at all. Even an eagle couldn't fly across it."

"Then that eagle must have been a fledgling?"

"Not at all. The shadow of his wings covers a whole city!"

"Then the city must be very small?"

"Not at all. A hare couldn't run from one end of it to the other!"

"Then that hare must be a very small one?"

"Not at all. Its hide would be large enough to make

a fur coat for a grown-up man, and a warm cap as well."

"Then the man must be a dwarf?"

"Not at all. If a cock were to crow at his feet, the sound of the cock's crowing would not reach the man's ears, he is so tall!"

"Then the man must be deaf?"

"Not at all. He could hear a deer grazing on a blade of grass, far away in the mountains."

The Monster was taken aback. He didn't know what other questions to ask. He stood there silently at the door for some time, then disappeared into the darkness.

The poor man and his wife were overjoyed.

When dawn was breaking, the youth prepared to take his leave.

"No, no, we can't let you go," cried the couple. You've saved our lives. Tell us what we can do to thank you."

"You don't have to thank me. Well, I must be on my way," replied the youth.

"Then at least tell us who you are," begged the man.

"Do you remember the proverb that says, 'Do good, and even if you throw it into the water, it will return to you some day?' I am that little talking fish that you pitied and threw back into the river!" said the youth. And before the couple had time to recover from their amazement, he had vanished.

1908

THE FOX THAT LOST ITS TAIL

ONCE UPON A TIME there lived an old woman. One day she milked her goat, put the pail down and went to fetch some firewood to boil the milk.

A Fox chanced by, and seeing the pail, stuck his head into it and lapped up all the milk.

The old woman flew at him with her chopper and chopped off his tail.

The fox ran off to a boulder, and crouching on it, began to plead with the old woman:

"Old lady, old lady, give me back my tail! I'll fix it in place again, and then I'll be able to return to my brethren. Otherwise they will make fun of me for being without a tail."

The old woman answered:

"You give me back my milk, and I'll give you back your tail."

The Fox ran up to the Cow, and said:

"Cow, kind Cow, please give me some milk. I'll give it to the old woman, and then she'll give me back my tail. I'll fix my tail in place again, and then I'll be able to return to my brethren. Otherwise they will make fun of me for being without a tail."

The Cow answered:

"Bring me some grass!"

So the Fox went to the Field.

"Field, my beautiful Field, please give me some grass! I'll take it to the Cow, and the Cow will give me some milk. I'll take the milk to the old woman, and she'll give me back my tail. I'll fix my tail in place again and then I'll be able to return to my brethren; otherwise they will make fun of me for being without a tail."

The Field replied:

"Fetch me some water!"

So the Fox went to a Stream and said:

"Stream, dear Stream, please give me some water! I'll take it to the Field, and the Field will give me some grass. I'll take the grass to the Cow, and the Cow will give me some milk. I'll take the milk to the old woman, and she'll give me back my tail. I'll fix my tail in place again, and then I'll be able to return to my brethren. Otherwise they will make fun of me for being without a tail."

The Stream answered:

"Bring me a jug!"

So the Fox went to a Maiden and pleaded:

"Maiden, fair Maiden, give me your jug! I'll take it to the Stream, and the Stream will give me some water. I'll take the water to Field, and the Field will give me some grass. I'll take the grass to the Cow, and the Cow will give me some milk. I'll take the milk to the old woman, and she'll give me back my tail. I'll fix my tail in place again, and then I'll be able to return to my brethren. Otherwise they will make fun of me for being without a tail."

The Maiden replied:

"Bring me some pretty beads!"

The Fox went to the Peddler, and pleaded for some beads.

"Peddler, kind Peddler, give me some pretty beads! I'll take the pretty beads to the Maiden, and she'll give me her jug. I'll take the jug to the Stream, and the Stream will give me some water. I'll take the water to the Field, and the Field will give me some grass. I'll take the grass to the Cow, and the Cow will give me some milk. I'll take the milk to the old woman, and she'll give me back my tail. I'll fix my tail in place again, and then I'll be able to return to my brethren. Otherwise they will make fun of me for being without a tail."

The Peddler answered:

"Bring me an egg!"

The Fox went to the Hen, and begged:

"Hen, my dear little Hen, give me an egg! I'll take the egg to the Peddler, and he'll give me some pretty beads. I'll take the pretty beads to the Maiden, and she'll give me her jug. I'll take the jug to the Stream, and the Stream will give me some water. I'll take the water to the Field, and the Field will give me some grass. I'll take the grass to the Cow, and the Cow will give me some milk. I'll take the milk to the old woman, and she'll give me back my tail. I'll fix my tail in place again, and then I'll be able to return to my brethren. Otherwise they will make fun of me for being without a tail."

The Hen said.

"Bring me some grain!"

The Fox went to the Thresher, and begged:

"Thresher, kind Thresher, give me some grain! I'll take the grain to the Hen, and she'll give me an egg. I'll take the egg to the Peddler, and he'll give me some pretty beads. I'll take the pretty beads to the Maiden, and she'll give me her jug. I'll take the jug to the Stream, and the Stream will give me some water. I'll take the water to the Field, and the Field will give me some grass. I'll take the grass to the Cow, and the Cow will give me some milk. I'll take the milk to the old woman, and she'll give me back my tail. Then I'll fix my tail in place again, and I'll be able to return to my brethren. Otherwise they will make fun of me for being without a tail."

The Thresher felt sorry for the poor Fox, and gave him a handful of grain.

So the Fox took the grain to the Hen, and the Hen gave him an egg. The Fox took the egg to the Peddler, and the Peddler gave him some pretty beads. The Fox took the pretty beads to the Maiden, and the Maiden gave him her jug. The Fox took her jug to the Stream, and the Stream gave him some water. The Fox took the water to the Field, and the Field gave him some grass. The Fox gave the grass to the Cow, and the Cow gave him some milk. The Fox took the milk to the old woman, and the old woman gave him back his tail.

The Fox fixed his tail in place again, and ran off to join his brethren, and none of them made fun of him.

1907